New Wave
English
in Practice

REVISED EDITION

DAILY SKILLS PRACTICE

4

This book belongs to:

New Wave English in Practice *(Book 4)*

Published by Prim-Ed Publishing 2014
Copyright© R.I.C. Publications® 2014
Revised and reprinted 2022
ISBN 978-1-80087-418-3
6223IR

Titles available in this series:
New Wave English in Practice *(Book 1)*
New Wave English in Practice *(Book 2)*
New Wave English in Practice *(Book 3)*
New Wave English in Practice *(Book 4)*
New Wave English in Practice *(Book 5)*
New Wave English in Practice *(Book 6)*
New Wave English in Practice Teacher Guide for Books 1–6

NOBODY DESERVES TO BE BULLIED.
TELL AN ADULT YOU CAN TRUST.

This anti-bullying campaign is supported by the Irish Educational Publishers' Association.

Contact details:

R.I.C. Publications

Australia
+61 9240 9888
www.ricpublications.com.au
mail@ricpublications.com.au

South Africa
+27 380 0267
www.ricpublications.co.za
sales@ricpublications.co.za

New Zealand
+64 3 356 1775
www.ricpublications.co.nz
mail@ricpublications.co.nz

Prim-Ed Publishing Ltd

Ireland
+353 051 440075
www.prim-ed.ie
sales@prim-ed.com

United Kingdom
+44 020 3773 9620
www.prim-ed.co.uk
sales@prim-ed.co.uk

FOREWORD

In this daily practice workbook you will be able to develop your ability to use English. Each day, you will have questions to answer in the areas of spelling, word study, punctuation and grammar. There are 160 days of questions in this workbook.

Seven weeks of each unit begin with a new skill focus. This will help remind you of some of the skills and terminology that will be used throughout the workbook. Every day, two questions will focus on the skill that is introduced at the start of the week. The remaining questions will be mixed practice which will help to improve your English skills as well as your knowledge about how language works.

At the completion of each unit, you will have the opportunity to review what you have learnt by doing one day of skill focus revision questions. Your daily scores are recorded in the bubble at the bottom of each day. These daily scores can be transferred onto the record sheets at the front of your book.

This will give an overview of your performance for the whole school year. Be sure to read each question carefully before you answer it. If you find a question too difficult, move on to the next one. If you have time at the end, you can go back to the one you haven't done.

CONTENTS

Record Sheet

Week 1		Week 2		Week 3		Week 4	
Date		Date		Date		Date	
Skill Focus		Skill Focus		Skill Focus		Skill Focus	
Day 1	12.	Day 1	-	Day 1		Day 1	
Day 2		Day 2		Day 2		Day 2	
Day 3		Day 3		Day 3		Day 3	
Day 4		Day 4		Day 4		Day 4	
Day 5		Day 5		Day 5		Day 5	

Week 5		Week 6		Week 7		Week 8	
Date		Date		Date		Date	
Skill Focus		Skill Focus		Skill Focus		Day 1	
Day 1		Day 1		Day 1		Day 2	
Day 2		Day 2		Day 2		Day 3	
Day 3		Day 3		Day 3		Day 4	
Day 4		Day 4		Day 4		Day 5	
Day 5		Day 5		Day 5		Revision	

Week 9		Week 10		Week 11		Week 12	
Date		Date		Date		Date	
Skill Focus		Skill Focus		Skill Focus		Skill Focus	
Day 1		Day 1		Day 1		Day 1	
Day 2		Day 2		Day 2		Day 2	
Day 3		Day 3		Day 3		Day 3	
Day 4		Day 4		Day 4		Day 4	
Day 5		Day 5		Day 5		Day 5	

Week 13		Week 14		Week 15		Week 16	
Date		Date		Date		Date	
Skill Focus		Skill Focus		Skill Focus		Day 1	
Day 1		Day 1		Day 1		Day 2	
Day 2		Day 2		Day 2		Day 3	
Day 3		Day 3		Day 3		Day 4	
Day 4		Day 4		Day 4		Day 5	
Day 5		Day 5		Day 5		Revision	

Record Sheet

Week 17		Week 18		Week 19		Week 20	
Date		*Date*		*Date*		*Date*	
Skill Focus		Skill Focus		Skill Focus		Skill Focus	
Day 1		Day 1		Day 1		Day 1	
Day 2		Day 2		Day 2		Day 2	
Day 3		Day 3		Day 3		Day 3	
Day 4		Day 4		Day 4		Day 4	
Day 5		Day 5		Day 5		Day 5	

Week 21		Week 22		Week 23		Week 24	
Date		*Date*		*Date*		*Date*	
Skill Focus		Skill Focus		Skill Focus		Day 1	
Day 1		Day 1		Day 1		Day 2	
Day 2		Day 2		Day 2		Day 3	
Day 3		Day 3		Day 3		Day 4	
Day 4		Day 4		Day 4		Day 5	
Day 5		Day 5		Day 5		Revision	

Week 25		Week 26		Week 27		Week 28	
Date		*Date*		*Date*		*Date*	
Skill Focus		Skill Focus		Skill Focus		Skill Focus	
Day 1		Day 1		Day 1		Day 1	
Day 2		Day 2		Day 2		Day 2	
Day 3		Day 3		Day 3		Day 3	
Day 4		Day 4		Day 4		Day 4	
Day 5		Day 5		Day 5		Day 5	

Week 29		Week 30		Week 31		Week 32	
Date		*Date*		*Date*		*Date*	
Skill Focus		Skill Focus		Skill Focus		Day 1	
Day 1		Day 1		Day 1		Day 2	
Day 2		Day 2		Day 2		Day 3	
Day 3		Day 3		Day 3		Day 4	
Day 4		Day 4		Day 4		Day 5	
Day 5		Day 5		Day 5		Revision	

Skill Focus

Day 1

Nouns and Proper Nouns

Different types of words are used in sentences to help share meaning.

Nouns are words that are used to name people, places, things, feelings or ideas.

person
boy
mother
doctor

thing
dog
chair
banana

feeling
surprise
sadness
fear

place
school
forest
city

idea
peace
religion
time

Some nouns start with capital letters. They are called **proper nouns**.

You can remember which nouns and other words need a capital letter using the 'M.I.N.T.S.' acronym:

M: Months, days and holidays

I: The word 'I'

N: Names of people and places

T: Titles of people, films, books and other things

S: Start of sentences

For example: **Jake, Mia** and **I** watched '**Harry Potter**' at
(names)   (word 'I')   (title)
the **Piccadilly Cinema** on **Tuesday**.
(place)   (day)

Practice Questions

1. Circle two nouns.

   I bought a ticket for the train.

2. Circle the proper nouns.

   On tuesday, the train travels directly from dublin to belfast.

1. Circle the noun.

   We really enjoy a long holiday.

2. Circle the proper nouns.

   Our favourite places to travel are France and Spain.

3. Circle the error and write correctly.

   It's my birthday tomorro.

   It's my birthday tomorrow

4. Write the plural of **fox**.

   foxes

5. An opposite of **despair** is

   hope

   disaster   hope   misery

6. Add **dis** to **respect**.

   disrespect

7. Circle the word that would come after **consider** in alphabetical order.

   complete   century   continue

8. Tick the meaning of the word **inhabit.**

   • to talk non-stop ☐

   • to live in a place ☑

9. Write the correct word.

   *I had a feeling of great **happy/happiness**.*

   happines

10. **tried** or **tired**?

    tried hard to finish all my work.

11. Is the word in bold a noun?

    yes ☐   no ☑

    *I picked up the **book** and put it on the table.*

12. How many capital letters are needed?

    we left new york and travelled to miami.

    4

    MY SCORE

Day 2

1. The noun in this sentence is [ ].
   They were all sitting around in the (park)

2. Circle the proper nouns.
   (Emma) (Ben) and (Joey) were playing a game of cricket.

3. Rearrange the letters to spell a word meaning *lady*.
   [w o m a n] n w o a m

4. Write the singular of *axes*.
   [Axe]

5. A similar meaning to *caught* is
   [Cauth]
   caused   escaped   captured

6. *fill* + *ing* = [filling]

7. Write the correct word.
   I was chased by a big brown *bare/bear*.
   [bear]

8. Shorten *do* and *not*. [don't]

9. Is the missing word *beauty* or *beautiful*?
   Its [beauty] amazed them all.

10. Add *of* or *off*.
    My hat blew [off] my head.

11. Is the word in bold a noun?
    yes [·]   no [✓]
    They thought that the crystal **cave** was unbelievably beautiful.

12. Add punctuation.
    My favourite sports are cricket, rugby
    and tennis [.]

Day 3

1. Circle the nouns.
   The old lady looked for a seat on the bus.

2. Circle the proper noun.
   (She) catches a bus to the shop every (Monday.)

3. Circle and rewrite the misspelt word.
   Dad put new furnature in my room.
   [furniture]

4. Write the plural of *maze*. [azes]

5. Circle an opposite of *polite*.
   exactly   (rude)   dishonest

6. Add *dis* to *appear*. [disappear]

7. Which word would come after *woman* in alphabetical order?
   (women)   (weight)   wallet

8. Tick the meaning of the word *souvenir*.
   • something kept as a reminder [✓]
   • something you eat [ ]

9. Is the missing word *happy* or *happiness*?
   The [happy] lady smiled at me.

10. *bought* or *brought*?
    We [bought] some fruit at the market.

11. Is the word in bold a noun?
    yes [✓]   no [ ]
    A man on the **bus** said I had good manners.

12. How many capital letters are needed? [4]
    on friday, we will visit my uncle james.

Day 4

1. Circle the nouns.

   I found my ball under the thick bushes.

2. Circle the proper nouns.

   My ball had been lost since February.

3. Rearrange the letters to spell a word meaning **unusual**.

   s [ ]   t r a g n e s

4. Write the singular of **churches**.

   [ ]

5. Circle the closest meaning to **identical.**

   different   matching   belonging

6. **fight** + **ing** = [ ]

7. Write the correct word.

   Be careful or you'll **brake/break** *it.* [ ]

8. Shorten **did** and **not**. [ ]

9. Circle the correct word.

   They all looked **miserable/misery** *as they left the party.*

10. Add **of** or **off**.

    I said, 'I know one [ ] *those boys'.*

11. Is the word in bold a noun?

    yes [ ]   no [ ]

    The group of **boys** *played football at the park.*

12. Add punctuation.

    Where did you buy those shoes [ ]

Day 5

1. The noun in this sentence is [ ].

   Did you make those cakes yesterday?

2. Circle the proper nouns.

   I made a special cake to celebrate Mum and Dad's anniversary.

3. Circle the error and write correctly.

   That singer's voyce is beautiful.

   [ ]

4. Write the plural of **wish**. [ ]

5. An opposite of **sincerely** is [ ].

   honestly   truly   falsely

6. Does the **re** in **return** and **redirect** mean under or again?

   [ ]

7. Which word would come after **height** in alphabetical order?

   heart   history   heard

8. Tick the meaning of the word **extraordinary**.

   • something that is special [ ]

   • something that is added [ ]

9. Is the missing word **tasty** or **taste**?

   I can't wait to have a [ ] *of it.*

10. **tried** or **tired**?

    I [ ] *to remember his name.*

11. Is the word in bold a noun?

    yes [ ]   no [ ]

    I have a new **recipe** *and I can't wait to try it.*

12. How many capital letters are needed? [ ]

    can you guess where ella and i went at the weekend?

MY SCORE [ ]   MY SCORE [ ]

Adjectives

Adjectives are words that describe nouns or pronouns (other words used for people, places or things).

They can be used before or after the words they are describing.

They help make writing clearer and more interesting.

There are many different types of adjectives.

Adjectives tell us:

what kind?	which one?
old watch	**left** hand
straw basket	**right** foot
rude children	**first** birthday
small mouse	**last** chocolate
green shirt	**other** shoes

how many? or how much?

three dogs
nine cats
some money
half a cake
several mistakes

To help you find or choose an adjective, look for the noun and ask yourself 'what kind', 'which one' or 'how many/much' is it?

Practice Questions

1. Circle the adjectives.

   The young, inexperienced pilot almost crashed.

2. Write the best adjective to describe the noun.

   [_____] explorers

   good   adventurous   productive

1. Circle two adjectives.

   The paper in our printer keeps jamming because it's old and damp.

2. Write the adjective to describe each noun.

   [_____] printer   [_____] business

   expensive   searching   wealthy

3. Rearrange the letters to spell a word meaning *to be sure*.

   [c _____]   t a c e n i r

4. Write the plural of *family*. Hint: change y to i and add es.   [_____]

5. Add *mis* to *print*.   [_____]

6. Which word would come before *queen* in alphabetical order?

   quiz   quarter   question

7. Tick the meaning of the word *occasionally*.

   • from time to time   ☐

   • often   ☐

8. *bought* or *brought*?

   Dad [_____] *computer paper home.*

9. Circle the noun.

   There is something wrong with our printer.

10. Is *cartridge* a noun or an adjective?

    *We need to replace the old **cartridge**.*

    [_____]

11. Is the missing word *care* or *carefully*?

    The books were printed with great

    [_____]

12. Add punctuation.

    How many copies would you like [☐]

    [☐]
    MY SCORE

Day 2

1 Circle the two adjectives.

   Tim's favourite uncle sent him exciting puzzles.

2. Write the adjective to describe each noun.

   [   ] parcel   [   ] puzzle

   large   challenging   busy

3. Circle and rewrite the misspelt word.

   I think this work is too dificult.

   [   ]

4. Write the plural of **fly**. [   ]

5. **slip** + **ing** = [   ]

   Hint: double the last letter before adding ing.

6. Write the correct word.

   *We collect our **male/mail** from the post office.*

   [   ]

7. Shorten **he** and **is**. [   ]

8. **too** or **to**?

   I think I have eaten [   ] *much cake!*

9. How many nouns in this sentence? [   ]

   Dad has been waiting for that parcel to arrive in the post.

10. Is **clouds** a noun or an adjective?

    *That difficult puzzle takes ages to do because there's so much white snow and lots of **clouds**.*

    [   ]

11. Write **puzzle** or **puzzling** in this sentence.

    I don't know the answer to this extremely

    [   ] *question.*

12. Add punctuation.

    Mum was angry because I had left all my puzzle pieces on the floor [   ]

Day 3

1. Circle the two adjectives.

   The horse is very young and energetic.

2. Write the adjective to describe each noun.

   [   ] horse   [   ] rider

   skilled   obedient   shiny

3. Rearrange the letters to spell a word meaning **place**.

   [p   ]   s t o i n i o p

4. Write the plural of **sky**. [   ]

5. Add **dis** to **obey**.

   [   ]

6. Write the correct word.

   *A **male/mail** horse is called a stallion.*

   [   ]

7. Tick the meaning of the word **ordinary**.

   • something that is very special   ☐

   • something usual or normal   ☐

8. **brought** or **bought**?

   I [   ] *some stickers from the shop.*

9. Circle the proper noun.

   Lisa has been riding horses since she was six.

10. Is **uncle** a noun or an adjective?

    *This saddle I'm using is an old one my **uncle** had on his farm.*

    [   ]

11. Write the word **ride** or **riding** in this sentence.

    Every Saturday afternoon I am allowed to have a long [   ] *lesson.*

12. Add punctuation.

    I really enjoy horse riding [   ]

MY SCORE   MY SCORE

Day 4

1. Circle two adjectives.

   Emma's bicycle is always kept clean and shiny.

2. Write the adjective to describe each noun.

   [ ] road   [ ] brakes

   busy   hungry   effective

3. Circle the error and write correctly.

   Can you ride a bycicle?

   [   ]

4. Write the plural of **baby** and **try**.

   [   ]   [   ]

5. **stop** + **ing** =

   [   ]

6. Which word would come after **disconnect** in alphabetical order?

   disrespect   disallow   disarray

7. Shorten **has** and **not.** [   ]

8. **too** or **to**?

   There are [   ] many things [   ] do before dinner.

9. Circle the proper noun.

   Emma has some new brakes on her bicycle.

10. Is the word in bold a noun or an adjective?

    *She did up the strap on her **new** helmet.*

    [   ]

11. Is the missing word **safe** or **safety**?

    Wearing a helmet keeps you [   ].

12. Add punctuation.

    Do you know how to follow the road rules [   ]

    [   ] MY SCORE

Day 5

1. Circle two adjectives.

   Good readers should read to young children.

2. Write the adjective to describe each noun.

   [ ] reading   [ ] book

   scary   fluent   turning

3. Rearrange the letters to spell a word that is a **type of picture**.

   [p   ]   p h o g h r t o a p

4. Write the plural of **lady** and **story**.

   [   ]   [   ]

5. Add **re** to **gain**.

   [   ]

6. Which word would come after **retract** in alphabetical order?

   regain   revise   report

7. Tick the meaning of the word **strange**.

   • something that is unusual or odd [   ]

   • something that is not wanted [   ]

8. **of** or **off**?

   Daniel fell [   ] *his bike.*

9. Circle the proper nouns.

   My clever sister can read Harry Potter books.

10. Is the word in bold a noun or an adjective?

    *I can't read big, **heavy** books in bed.*

    [   ]

11. Use **exciting** or **excitement** in this sentence.

    The reader's [   ] *showed.*

12. Add punctuation.

    It's really exciting [   ]

    [   ] MY SCORE

Pronouns

Other words are often used in sentences to replace the noun.

These words are called **pronouns**.

There are many different types of pronouns. They can refer to people, objects and animals.

The pronoun that is used depends on whether the noun being replaced refers to:

• yourself
• a person, object or animal
• a male or female
• one or more people or things

	Only one	Part of a group
yourself	I, me	us, we
male	he, him, you	they, them
female	she, her, you	they, them
object/animal	it	they, them

Using pronouns in your writing is all about balance.

Make sure that you do not use too many, or your writing will not be clear.

They saw **them** playing with **it**.

Make sure that you use enough, or your writing will be repetitive.

Mum and Anna went to the shop, and **Mum and Anna** bought some fruit.

Practice Questions

1. Circle two pronouns.

   We saw a rabbit, but it raced away.

2. **we** or **us**?

   Do you know where [____] *are going?*

1. Circle the pronoun.

   John likes pizza. He doesn't like pasta.

2. **me** or **I**?

   She said [____] *could use her new pencils.*

3. Circle the error and write correctly.

   His escape was amazeing.

   [____]

4. Write the plural of **calf**.
   Hint: change f to v and add es. [____]

5. **slam** + **ing** = [____]

6. Which word would come after **disappoint** in alphabetical order?

   dislike   disappear   disability

7. Tick the meaning of the word **quay**.

   • a wharf where ships are unloaded ☐
   • something used to unlock things ☐

8. **his** or **he's**?

   What's [____] *name?*

9. Circle two nouns.

   The old ship slowly entered the icy harbour.

10. Circle three adjectives.

    The ship's young crew felt proud and excited.

11. Write the adjective to describe the noun.

    [____] sails

    sparkling   billowing   tasty

12. Add punctuation.

    The sailors had been travelling for a

    long time [____]

MY SCORE

Day 2

1. Circle the pronoun.

   Mary didn't go. She was sick.

2. **he** or **him**?

   I don't like the way [_____] *speaks to me.*

3. Rearrange the letters to spell a word that is a **number**.

   [h _____]   d r u n e d h

4. Write the plural of **elf**.

   [_____]

5. Add **dis** to **belief**. [_____]

6. Which word would come after **straight** in alphabetical order?

   stray   stomach   seize   science

7. Circle the opposite of **ordinary.**

   semiordinary   participation   extraordinary

8. Write **lend** or **borrow**.

   Can I please [_____] *your phone?*

9. Circle two nouns.

   The snow-tipped mountain glistened in the sunlight.

10. Circle the adjectives.

    The exhausted climbers reached the distant summit.

11. Write the adjective to describe the noun.

    [_____] snow

    powdery   spectacular   ragged

12. Add capital letters.

    their next challenge was to climb the famous mount everest.

    [_____]

    MY SCORE

Day 3

1. Circle the pronoun.

   I don't think the film is funny.

2. **she** or **her**?

   Did [_____] *climb alone?*

3. Circle and rewrite the misspelt word.

   Please anser the question.

   [_____]

4. Write the plural of **shelf**. [_____]

5. **run** + **ing** = [_____]

6. Write the correct word.

   She gave me a tasty **piece/peace** *of apple pie.*

   [_____]

7. Tick the meaning of the word **summit**.

   • something that is not deep   ▢

   • highest point of a mountain   ▢

8. Add **it's** or **its**.

   I said, 'I think [_____] *a delicious pie'.*

9. The noun in the sentence is [_____].

   We had an unusual sandwich and decided it was the tastiest.

10. Circle the two adjectives.

    We made a moist, delicious cake out of butter, flour, eggs and sugar.

11. Is **open** a noun or an adjective?

    I smelt a fruit pie cooking through the **open** *window.*

    [_____]

12. Add punctuation.

    I absolutely love apple pie [___]

    What's your favourite flavour [___]

    MY SCORE

Day 4

1. Circle two pronouns.

   Can you see it now?

2. **we** or **us**?

   Would you like to play a game with [_____]?

3. Rearrange the letters to spell a word meaning **apart**.

   [s _____] s p r t a e e a

4. Write the plural of **thief** and **wife**.

   [_____] [_____]

5. Add **mis** to **place**. [_____]

6. Write the correct word.

   The excited dog raced off to **bury/berry** *the bone.*

   [_____]

7. Circle a similar meaning to **refunding**.

   remaining   keeping   returning

8. Add **it's** or **its**.

   The dog took [_____] *bone into the garden.*

9. The noun in the sentence is [_____].

   The noisy animal barked until it was exhausted.

10. Circle the three adjectives.

    The poor dog wandered into the garden looking hungry and miserable.

11. Is **present** a noun or an adjective?

    This adorable puppy was a **present** *from my uncle.*

    [_____]

12. Add capital letters.

    we called the puppy max.

    [_____]

MY SCORE

Day 5

1. Circle two pronouns.

   We asked our new neighbours to play with us.

2. **me** or **I**?

   Give it to [_____]!

3. Circle the error and write correctly.

   I interveiwed her myself.

   [_____]

4. Write the plural of **half** and **loaf**.

   [_____] [_____]

5. **skip** + **ing** = [_____]

6. Circle the word which would come before **century** in alphabetical order.

   certain   centre   circle

7. Tick the meaning of the word **possession**.

   • a line of people moving along   ▢

   • something belonging to a person   ▢

8. Write **lend** or **borrow**.

   Could you [_____] *me your camera?*

9. Circle two nouns.

   We watched the parade from our window.

10. Circle three adjectives.

    Happy, laughing people danced on colourful floats.

11. Write the adjective to describe each noun.

    [_____] music [_____] faces

    smiling   towering   loud

12. Add punctuation.

    Why is it so noisy [_]

    Wow, look at that one [_]

MY SCORE

Verbs and Tense

A verb is a word which shows actions, or states of being or having.

We **_ran_** to the train station.

(action)

Sarah **is** the best football player.

(being)

We **_have_** a new teacher for music.

(having)

Every sentence must have a verb.

Most verbs change their form, depending on who is doing the action and the **tense**.

Tense tells whether the verb happens in the past, present (now) or future.

← PAST	▼ PRESENT ▼	FUTURE →
ed is usually added to words that have already happened (e.g. play → played). Sometimes the word changes completely (e.g. buy → bought).	The word may stay the same or the endings **s** or **ing** may be added (e.g. play/plays/is playing).	The word **will** is added before the verb (e.g. will play).

When choosing the correct verb form, remember to re-read the sentence to make sure it makes sense.

Practice Questions

1. Circle the verbs.

   The handsome actor waved at the crowd as they cheered his name.

2. Is the verb in the **past/present/future** tense?

   The photographers took many photos of the popular superstar.

1. Circle the verbs.

   Crabs look for food by digging holes in the soft sand.

2. Is the verb in the **present/past/future** tense?

   The crabs eat small fish and algae.

3. Rearrange the letters to spell a word meaning **_not easy_**.

   d _____ f f i u c i t l d

4. Write the plural of **_shelf_**.

   _____

5. Circle a similar meaning to **_ordinary_**.

   special   common   spectacular

6. Circle the word which would come after **_build_** in alphabetical order.

   business   believe   bicycle

7. Tick the meaning of the word **_experience_**.

   • something that happens to you ☐

   • a journey of exploration ☐

8. **_me_** or **_I_**?

   She wouldn't give it to _____ .

9. Circle two nouns.

   Early explorers discovered some new countries.

10. Circle three adjectives.

    Magnificent, tall, straight trees covered the land.

11. Circle two pronouns.

    Where did they put it?

12. Add the missing punctuation.

    he crossed the swiss alps

MY SCORE

Day 2

1. Circle two verbs.

   My horse loves the carrots we give him every morning.

2. Is the verb in the **present/past/future** tense?

   Every afternoon, he gallops around the field.

3. Circle and rewrite the misspelt word.

   The strange experament worked.

   [   ]

4. Write the plural of **clock** and **lunch**.

   [   ] [   ]

5. An opposite of **complete** is [   ].

   ended   complicated   unfinished

6. Write the correct word. [   ]

   *We crossed the **dessert/desert** in three days.*

7. Shorten **would** and **have**. [   ]

8. Add **a** or **an**.
   Hint: use **an** before a word that starts with a vowel.

   It is [   ] *interesting book.*

9. The noun in this sentence is [   ].

   Breathing in that hot, dry air was painful.

10. Circle the three adjectives.

    We found cool water near the large, shady trees.

11. Is **water** a noun or an adjective?

    The thirsty camels were in a hurry to reach the **water**.

    [   ]

12. Add the missing punctuation.

    i sat in the shade for a while before i started my journey again

Day 3

1. Circle two verbs.

   We took the boat out and caught some fish yesterday.

2. Is the verb in the **present/past/future** tense?

   The old men have fished here almost every weekend.

3. Rearrange the letters to spell a word that means **correct** and **precise**.

   [a   ] u c c r t a e a

4. Write the plural of **reply**.

   [   ]

5. Circle a similar meaning to **knowledge**.

   ignorance   understanding   remembrance

6. Write the correct word. [   ]

   *I can't wait to eat that yummy **dessert/desert**.*

7. Tick the meaning of the word **shallow**.

   • something that is not deep   ☐
   • something that is not seen   ☐

8. **me** or **I**?

   Sue and [   ] *are late for school.*

9. The noun in this sentence is [   ].

   I thought the light, fluffy cakes were delicious.

10. Circle the three adjectives.

    Kim's favourite dessert is vanilla ice cream covered in chocolate sauce.

11. Circle the word the pronoun **it** is taking the place of.

    *She licked the spoon after scraping the bowl with **it**.*

12. Add punctuation.

    How do I get there [☐]

    No, not that way [☐]

Day 4

1. Circle two verbs.

   The school gardener cut some pink flowers and put them in our classroom.

2. Is the verb in the **present/past/future** tense?

   We enjoyed the scent of the beautiful bouquet.

3. Circle the spelling errors and write correctly.

   I promis I'll come strait home.

   [ ]   [ ]

4. Circle the correct plurals.   **babys** or **babies**

   flys or **flies**

5. An opposite of **tough** is [ ].

   strong   treated   tender

6. Circle the word which comes before **peculiar** in alphabetical order.

   perhaps   position   particular

7. Shorten **I** and **will**. [ ]

8. Add **a** or **an**.

   His careless driving caused [ ] *accident.*

9. Circle three nouns.

   Grabbing their bags, the children rushed to the bus.

10. Write the adjective to describe each noun.

    [ ] children   [ ] bags

    packed   tasty   noisy

11. Is **new** a noun or an adjective?

    *The tired, old bus needs a **new** engine.*

    [ ]

12. How many words need capital letters? [ ]

    The bus driver, mr brown, drove us to our school in sydney.

    MY SCORE

Day 5

1. Circle the verbs.

   The children have packed their bags and tidied their desks.

2. Is the verb in the **present/past/future** tense?

   They will go home shortly.

3. Rearrange the letters to spell a word that means to think someone is **special**.

   [a   ]   m i d e r a

4. Write the plural of **match** and **finch**.

   [ ]   [ ]

5. A similar meaning to **mention** is [ ].

   tell   mend   silence

6. Circle the word which comes before **thought** in alphabetical order.

   threw   though   through

7. Tick the meaning of the word **guard**.

   • to look carefully at something   [ ]

   • to protect and keep safe   [ ]

8. **me** or **I**?

   That's the one Ben and [ ] *borrowed.*

9. Circle three nouns.

   There are many books in our school's new library.

10. Write the adjective to describe each noun.

    [ ] hero   [ ] castle

    crying   majestic   brave

11. Circle two pronouns.

    May I please borrow it?

12. How many words need capital letters? [ ]

    The hero, harry, lived in the united states of america.

    MY SCORE

Skill Focus

Day 1

Plural Nouns

A **plural** is a word used to show more than one of something.

When we have only one, it is called **singular**.

When we want to make a plural noun, we usually add s or es.

There are some words that have different rules. Let's take a closer look at some of these.

Words ending in y

When a word ends in a vowel followed by y—just add s.

monkey → monkey**s**

When a word ends in a consonant followed by y—change y to i and add es.

butterfly → butterfl̶y̶ⁱ**es**

Words ending with f or fe

Usually we change the f/fe to v and add es.

knife → knif̶e̶ᵛ**es**

Sometimes we just add an s.

reef → reef**s**

Words ending with o

Usually when a word ends in a consonant followed by o—add es.

potato → potato**es**

When a word ends in a vowel followed by o—just add s.

radio → radio**s**

Practice Questions

Write the plurals of these words.

1. play [ ]   baby [ ]

2. sniff [ ]   calf [ ]

3. hero [ ]   zoo [ ]

---

1. Write the plural of *lady*.

   [ ]

2. Write the plural of *key*.

   [ ]

3. Circle the spelling error.

   They herd a strange noise.

   Write the word correctly. [ ]

4. *smile* + *ing* =
   Hint: drop the
   e before adding ing. [ ]

5. An opposite of *caught* is [ ].

   released   captured   held

6. Which word would come before *address* in alphabetical order?

   answer   appear   actual

7. Tick the meaning of the word *coast*.

   • thick or rough   [ ]
   • land beside the sea   [ ]

8. Write the correct word. [ ]

   He **rode/rowed** the boat ashore.

9. Add the missing pronoun.

   Pets are great but you have to

   look after [ ].

10. The pronoun **he** refers to [ ].

    *Tom has ten fish, but **he** often forgets to feed them.*

11. Add the correct verb. **riding/ridden**

    This horse is [ ] *every day.*

12. Add punctuation.

    i havent got any pets. do you

    [MY SCORE]

Day 2

1. Write the plural of **potato**.

2. Write the plural of **zoo**.

3. Rearrange the letters to spell a word meaning **bravery**.

   c   a g r o u e c

4. Add **dis** to **place**.

5. A similar meaning to build is

   construct   destroy   dismantle

6. Add the correct word **fare/fair**.

   We paid the driver our _____,
   then hopped on the bus.

7. Shorten **I** and **would**.

8. Add **edition** or **addition** to complete the sentence.

   We have a new _____ of that
   book.

9. Add the missing pronoun.

   He caught a small fish, but _____
   had to release it.

10. The pronoun **it** refers to _____.

    Dad's boat is old, but he thinks it is great.

11. Add the correct verb. **flying/flies**

    Our speedboat was _____
    across the water.

12. How many capital letters are needed? ☐

    we named our boat mary lou.

Day 3

1. Write the plural of **life.**

2. Write the plural of **cliff**.

3. Circle the spelling error. Write the word correctly.

   Are you certin about it?

4. **hide** + **ing** =

5. Make the opposite of **happy** by adding two letters.

6. Which word is first in alphabetical order?

   gathering   gadget   goodbye   giant

7. Tick the meaning of the word **pressure**.

   • an applied force   ☐
   • a special gift   ☐

8. Write the correct word.

   Are you **shore/sure** this is the place?

9. Which pronoun is missing?

   me or **I**

   Dad took Tim and _____ to the circus.

10. The pronoun **they** refers to _____.

    The clown is juggling balls with one hand. I
    wonder if they will fall?

11. Add the correct verb. **did/done**

    He _____ a spectacular cartwheel.

12. Add punctuation.

    im so happy that we went to the circus

Day 4

1. Write the plural of **sky**.

2. Write the plural of **monkey**.

3. Rearrange the letters to spell a word meaning **a person who investigates.**

   d [   ] t e c i e v t e d

4. Add **pre** to **historic**.

5. A similar meaning to **cavity** is

   [   ].

   carving   hollow   cause

6. Add the correct word. **fare/fair**

   She has very [   ] hair.

7. Shorten **we** and **had**.

8. Add **edition** or **addition** to complete the sentence.

   The new puppy was a welcome

   [   ] to our family.

9. Which pronoun is missing? **me** or **I**

   Paul and [   ] played with the puppy.

10. The pronoun **it** refers to [   ].

    The naughty puppy was barking all night, so it was exhausted by morning.

11. Add the correct verb. **did/done**

    The pup has [   ] naughty things.

12. Circle the letters that need to be capitals.

    we all love playing with emma's new puppy, rex.

MY SCORE

Day 5

1. Write the plural of **tomato**.

2. Write the plural of **photo**.

3. Circle and rewrite the misspelt word.

   Would you like to eat a biscit?

   [   ]

4. **flake** + **ing** = [   ]

5. Make the opposite of **disobedient** by removing some letters.

   [   ]

6. Which word is first in alphabetical order?

   virtual   visual   vein   village

7. Tick the meaning of the word **learn**.

   • to get knowledge   ☐
   • facts and figures   ☐

8. Write the correct word. [   ]

   Tie a **knot/not** in this rope.

9. Add the missing pronoun.

   Look at those insects, [   ] are everywhere.

10. The pronoun **them** refers to [   ].

    There were many flowers that had bees buzzing around them.

11. Add the correct verb. **collect/collecting**

    The bees are [   ] the nectar.

12. Add punctuation.

    i dont like it when the bees fly near me

MY SCORE

Speech Marks

Speech marks are used to show the *exact* words that are spoken by a person.

This is sometimes called **direct speech**. For example:

'I lost my wallet!' Dad exclaimed.

In this sentence, the exact words said by Dad (including the punctuation) are enclosed in speech marks.

Speech marks only enclose punctuation when the direct speech ends with an exclamation mark or question mark.

Otherwise, the speech marks only surround the words that were *actually* said:

'Your wallet is over here', said Ash.

Dad replied, 'I hadn't thought to look there'.

Any other words (like the speaker) that are not part of the direct speech don't go inside the speech marks.

A comma is used before or after the speaker.

A full stop is used if the speech ends the sentence.

Practice Questions

1. Add speech marks to show direct speech.

   We are picking up our new puppy this afternoon, Mum said.

2. Are the speech marks used correctly?

   yes ☐   no ☐

   'I can't wait! What should we call him'? I replied excitedly.

---

1. Add speech marks to show direct speech.

   He yelled, Hold on tight!

2. Are the speech marks used correctly?

   yes ☐   no ☐

   She shouted back, 'Give me your hand'!

3. Rearrange the letters to spell a word that means **26 letters.**

   a [   ]   a p l a b t e h

4. Circle the correct plurals.

   potatoes/potatos   tos/toes

5. Add **ion** to **separate.** Write the new word.

   [   ]

6. Which word would come after **interest** in alphabetical order?

   imagine   island   increase

7. Tick the meaning of the word **coarse**.

   • thick or rough   ☐
   • land beside the sea   ☐

8. Write a word that sounds the same as **brake** but is spelt differently.

   [   ]

9. Add the missing pronoun.

   That crumb is as big as the ant that's carrying

   [   ]

10. **breath** or **breathe**?

    Ants [   ] *through tiny holes in their sides called spiracles.*

11. The pronoun **they** refers to [   ].

    The ants will work hard all day until they have enough food for their nest.

12. Add commas.
    Hint: Use a comma between each item in a list.

    Peter bought an apple orange banana and kiwi for his lunch.

    MY SCORE [   ]

Day 2

1. Add speech marks to show direct speech.

   Why didn't they ask me to go? I whispered sadly to myself.

2. Are the speech marks used correctly?

   yes ☐   no ☐

   'Don't be sad!' We could play together, said a shy boy.

3. Circle the spelling error. Write it correctly.

   She looks very suprised.

4. Which word does not change f to v and add es to make its plural?

   life or **cliff**

5. The **dis** in **disappear** and **disrespect** means the opposite or double?

6. Shorten **he** and **would**.

7. An opposite of **tough** is

   strong   weak   terrible

8. Write **cellar** or **seller**.

   Mum got a great bargain from the

   in the market.

9. Which tense? **past/present/future**

   I will climb up those steep cliffs.

10. **breath** or **breathe**?

    I can't keep climbing. I'm out of

11. Circle the past tense of **sell**.   **sold** or **selled**

12. Add commas.

    Rita took Alan Sam Adam and Chloe on a hike.

Day 3

1. Add speech marks.

   Can we stop here and rest before we continue on our journey? he begged.

2. Are the speech marks used correctly?

   yes ☐   no ☐

   'We haven't got any time to spare!' replied Dad.

3. Rearrange the letters to spell a word that means **a surgical procedure**.

   o   e r p a i o t n o

4. Circle the incorrect plural.

   bamboos   kangarooes   shampoos

5. Add **al** to **nature** to make an adjective that means **real**.

6. Which word is last in alphabetical order?

   attack   atmosphere   assembly

7. Does this sentence make sense?

   yes ☐   no ☐

   The man climbed to the summit of the mountain.

8. Add the correct word. **missed/mist**

   We   our flight.

9. Circle the pronoun.

   We have been flying for seven hours.

10. Write **give** or **gave** to complete the sentence.

    The flight attendant   me a drink.

11. The pronoun **I** refers to

    Elly said, 'This is my first family holiday. I am so excited!'

12. How many words in the sentence are missing capital letters?

    I would really like to go to los angeles in february and visit disneyland park.

Day 4

1. Add speech marks.

   Please, please can't I just have one more apple muffin? Jason begged.

2. Are the speech marks used correctly?

   yes ☐   no ☐

   'You have had enough for one day', said Mum.

3. Circle and rewrite the misspelt word.

   The storm caused great damige.

   ☐

4. Which word doesn't have **ies** in its plural?

   valley   country   tummy   comedy

   ☐

5. The **re** in **recall** and **redo** means like or again?

   ☐

6. Shorten **she** and **had**.

   ☐

7. Circle a similar meaning to **prevent**.

   stop   change   present

8. Write **cellar** or **seller**.

   The old furniture was put down into the

   ☐

9. Which tense? **past/present/future**

   I am looking at those clouds.

10. Write **gives** or **gave** to complete the sentence.

    When the captain ☐ *his permission, I will go ashore.*

11. Circle the past tense of **buy. buyed** or **bought**

12. How many capital letters are needed? ☐

    would you like to ski on christmas day?

Day 5

1. Add speech marks.

   My friend asked, Does your puppy like going to the park to play?

2. Are the speech marks used correctly?

   yes ☐   no ☐

   'My pup loves to play fetch', I told her.

3. Rearrange the letters to spell a word which is a **measurement of distance**.

   k ☐   k o l m t r e i e

4. Circle the incorrect plural.

   potatoes   tomatoes   zooes

5. Add **ion** to **dictate**. Write the new word.

   ☐

6. Which word is first in alphabetical order?

   approach   agree   although

7. Tick the meaning of the word **punctual**.

   • being on time   ☐

   • full stops and capital letters   ☐

8. Write the correct word.

   *Those plants have **groan/grown** very well.*

   ☐

9. Add the missing pronoun.

   After school, Mum and ☐ *will go to the garden centre.*

10. **it's** or **its**?

    This rose is beautiful. What is ☐ *name?*

11. The pronoun **you** refers to ☐ .

    'Mum, I have finished all the weeding for you', I said.

12. Add commas.

    Dad put tea coffee sugar and jam in the cupboard.

Skill Focus

Rules for Adding Endings

Often, endings are added to base words to make a new word.

base word	+	endings beginning with consonants -s -tion -ly -sion -ful -ness -less -ship -ty -ment	=	new word
		endings beginning with vowels -es -est -ed -er -ing -y -ous -ish -able -ible		

These are some of the rules that most words follow when an ending is added.

Consonant and vowel endings + base words ending in consonant then y

Change y to i then add the ending:

copy^{i} + ed = copied

We don't do this when we add **ing**.

Vowel endings + base words ending with silent e

Drop the e then add the ending:

vacate + ion = vacation

Vowel endings + base words ending with a short vowel then consonant

Double the consonant before adding the ending:

hop$^{(+p)}$ing = hopping

For two syllable words, only double the final consonant if the final syllable is stressed (e.g. be<u>gin</u> or for<u>get</u> *not* <u>gar</u>den or <u>vis</u>it).

Practice Questions

1. Add **ing** to these words.

   (a) cry ☐   (b) wave ☐

   (c) stop ☐   (d) garden ☐

2. Add **ness** to these words.

   (a) happy ☐   (b) rude ☐

   (c) sad ☐

Day 1

1. *lazy* + *ly* = ☐

2. *try* + *ing* = ☐

3. Circle the error and write it correctly.

   He's an inportant man.

   ☐

4. Write a word that sounds the same as **bear** but is spelt differently.

   ☐

5. An opposite of **strength** is

   ☐.

   weakness   power   straightforward

6. Which word is second in alphabetical order?

   ☐

   believe   business   build   bicycle

7. Tick the meaning of the word **imagine**.

   • to form a picture in your mind   ☐

   • to make a copy of something   ☐

8. Write the verb. ☐

   I play the guitar.

9. Circle the two adjectives.

   My new guitar sounds fantastic.

10. Circle the correct word.

    *Dad went into town and **brought/bought** it for me.*

11. Write the correct word.

    *We usually **encounter/practise** at my friend's house.*

    ☐

12. Tick the sentence that has the correct punctuation.

    • 'Wow, it's amazing!' I exclaimed.   ☐

    • 'Wow, it's amazing! I exclaimed.'   ☐

MY SCORE

Day 2

1. Add *ing* to *forget* and *begin*.

2. Circle the correct spelling.

   admited   admitted

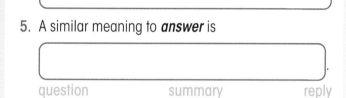

3. Rearrange the letters to spell a word meaning *not crooked*.

   s   r a g h i t t s

4. Write a word that sounds the same as *rode* but is spelt differently.

5. A similar meaning to *answer* is

   question   summary   reply

6. Which word is last in alphabetical order?

   naughty   natural   notice   none

7. Tick the meaning of the word *famous*.

   • widely known ⬚
   • important   ⬚

8. Write the verb.

   My family often drive to the country for the weekend.

9. Circle two adjectives.

   It will probably be a long, boring trip.

10. Circle the correct verb.

    *We **took/take** a huge caravan.*

11. Circle the correct word.

    *The man who **lent/borrowed** us the caravan is very kind.*

12. Tick the sentence that has the correct punctuation.

    • My sister kept asking 'Are we there yet!' ⬚
    • My sister kept asking, 'Are we there yet?' ⬚

MY SCORE

Day 3

1. *begin* + *ing* =

2. *ship* + *ment* =

3. Circle and rewrite the misspelt word.

   That histery book is amazing.

4. Write the plurals of *tomato* and *piano*.

5. Circle a similar meaning to *unique*.

   universal   undone   different

6. Write the correct word.

   *I watched the boys kicking a **ball/bawl** around.*

7. Shorten *does* and *not*.

8. Write the verb.

   The determined football players ran onto the field.

9. Is *slow* an adjective or a noun?

   *Our captain is a **slow** runner but he scores great goals.*

10. Add the correct past tense of *bring*.

    *The opposing team **bringed/brought/brang** many supporters with them.*

11. *was* or *were*?

    We [   ] trying very hard to win the football match.

12. Add a comma.

    We had cold drinks oranges and apples after the match.

MY SCORE

Day 4

1. Add *ing* to *garden* and *park*.

2. Circle the correct spelling.

   flavourred   flavoured

3. Rearrange the letters to spell a word that means the **highest point of a mountain**.

   [s   ] m i t m u s

4. Write the plurals of **company** and **turkey**.

5. Circle a similar meaning to **league**.

   group   leave   leak

6. Write the correct word.

   *If you take his toys away, he will **ball/bawl**.*

7. Shorten **have** and **not**.

8. Write the verb.

   My little brother is waiting at the front door.

9. Circle two adjectives.

   My little brother has a new friend visiting.

10. Add the correct past tense of **go. goed/gone/went**

    We all [   ]
    to the park at 3 o'clock.

11. **was** or **were**?

    The young children [   ]
    playing happily on the swings.

12. Add a comma.

    The dirty exhausted but happy children fell asleep on the way home.

Day 5

1. *hide* + *ing* =

2. *safe* + *ly* =

3. Circle the error and write correctly.

   I can't remenber his name.

4. Write a word that sounds the same as **mail** but is spelt differently.

5. An opposite of **believe** is [   ].

   doubt   accept   trust

6. Write the word in alphabetical order after **complete**.

   complex   comment   combine

7. Tick the meaning of the word **combine**.

   • to mix or join   ☐
   • to comb your own hair   ☐

8. Write the verb.

   The big waves at the beach scare me.

9. Circle three adjectives.

   A big wave washed my red football into the salty water.

10. Circle the correct word.

    *I wished I hadn't **brought/bought** it with me.*

11. Write the correct verb.

    *The busy bee **fly/flies** from flower to flower.*

12. Circle the sentence with correct punctuation.

    'Oh no, it's gone!' I cried.

    'Oh no, it's gone' I cried

MY SCORE

MY SCORE

Day 1

1. Rearrange the letters to spell a word meaning a **big shaking of the ground**.

   e [_____] e r h t a q a e k u

2. Circle the correct word. **mail/male**

   A ram is a [_____] sheep.

3. Add **ing** to **parent** and **study**.

   [_____] [_____]

4. An opposite of **separate** is [_____].

   together   single   alone

5. Which word is second in alphabetical order?

   quarter   question   quick

6. Tick the meaning of the word **quote**.

   • to make fun of a person   ☐

   • to repeat someone else's words ☐

7. Shorten **you** and **would**.

   [_____]

8. Circle the verb and its tense.

   We moved to a new house in a quieter street.

   past   present   future

9. Circle the pronoun and the noun it refers to.

   My parents said they will buy a new car in January.

10. Circle the correct word.

    I **seen/saw** the new house yesterday and it's great.

11. Cross out the word that does not belong.

    My new bedroom will be in upstairs.

12. Add punctuation.

    can I paint my new room green

Day 2

1. Circle and rewrite the misspelt word.

   His general knowlege is impressive.

   [_____]

2. Circle the incorrect plural.

   zoos   pianos   tomatos   heroes

3. **visit + ing** = [_____]

4. Circle an opposite of **fascinate**.

   enchant   fasten   bore

5. Write the correct word. [_____]

   We are not **allowed/aloud** to watch TV before school.

6. Write **past** or **passed**.

   The programme starts at half [_____] eight tonight.

7. **Won't** is a shortened word for

   [_____] and [_____].

8. Circle the verb and its tense.

   The hens roam around our garden all day.

   past   present   future

9. Circle four adjectives.

   My favourite hen is bossy, fat and white.

10. **its** or **it's**?

    Only one hen has built [_____] nest.

11. Cross out the word that does not belong.

    The hens laid a eggs this week.

12. Add punctuation.

    our three hens are named henny penny and brenda.

Day 3

1. Rearrange the letters to spell a word meaning *needing attention now.*

   [u _____] u g r e t n

2. Circle the incorrect plural.

   bamboos   cargoes   shampooes   kangaroos

3. *garden* + *ing* = [_____]

4. Circle the opposite of *deep.*

   long   shallow   surface

5. Write the correct word.

   *How much luggage are we **allowed/aloud?***

   [_____]

6. Write *past* or *passed.*

   We [_____] our tickets to the flight attendant.

7. Shorten *they* and *have.*

   [_____]

8. Circle the verb and its tense.

   A polite man drove us to the airport.

   past   present   future

9. Circle the pronoun and the noun it refers to.

   The flight attendant said she will be handing out snacks soon.

10. *its* or *it's?*

    I don't know if [_____] *time to move around the cabin.*

11. Cross out the word that does not belong.

    The noise of the plane that was annoying.

12. Add punctuation.

    our flight from dublin to new york was long.

Day 4

1. Circle the error and write it correctly.

   She led an ordinery life.

   [_____]

2. Does *mis* in the words *misinform, misspell* and *mispronounce* mean wrong **or** little?

   [_____]

3. Add *ed* to *visit* and *neglect.*

   [_____] [_____]

4. The opposite of selfish is [_____].

   people   generous   confidence

5. Which word is second in alphabetical order?

   prepare   predict   prefix   present

6. Tick the meaning of the word *technology.*

   • things that have to do with ancient history ☐

   • up-to-date computers and machinery ☐

7. *Weren't* is a shortened word for

   [_____] and [_____].

8. Circle the verb and its tense.

   We went to the library today.

   past   present   future

9. Circle three adjectives.

   Ian's favourite book was about a brave, honest hero who tried to help others.

10. *is, am* or *are?*

    We [_____] *allowed to visit the library at lunchtime too.*

11. Cross out the word that does not belong.

    In the every afternoon, we can read books outside.

12. Add punctuation.

    i asked, Can we read now

Day 5

1. Rearrange the letters to spell a word that means *things that happened in the past.*

   h _____ s h i r y o t

2. Add the same three letters to **behave** and **lead** to make them their opposites.

   _____ _____

3. Add **ed** to **prefer** and **admit**.

   _____ _____

4. An opposite of **mistake** is _____ .

   false   correct   incorrect

5. Which word is last in alphabetical order?

   broke   beginning   burst   borrow

6. Tick the meaning of the word **banquet**.

   • a place people are not allowed to go ☐
   • a large, formal dinner ☐

7. Shorten **who** and **has**.

   _____

8. Circle the verb and its tense.

   Mum hired a clown for my party.

   past   present   future

9. Circle the pronoun and the noun it refers to.

   My best friend's brother is also coming because he loves clowns.

10. **is, am** or **are**?

    I hope he _____ *coming to my birthday party.*

11. Cross out the word that does not belong.

    The clown's performance was the best act I have ever not seen.

12. Add punctuation.

    how wonderful Can you do it again

Skill Focus Review

1. Circle the error and write it correctly.

   I will visit my aunt after school tomorro.

   _____

2. Write the plurals of **donkey** and **party**.

   _____ _____

3. The **un** in **unkind** and **unbelievable** means from or not? _____

4. Add these endings to **happy**.

   happy + ly = _____

   happy + er = _____

5. Write the noun and proper noun.

   _____ _____

   Timothy had lost his new hat.

6. Circle the proper nouns that need a capital letter.

   His teacher, mrs greene, said timothy had to find it before lunchtime.

7. Circle three adjectives.

   Timothy searched through his messy desk. He felt something wet and slimy.

8. Add the correct adjective. **disgusting** or **lovely**

   He had left a _____ *, mouldy banana in his desk.*

9. Circle the pronoun and the noun it refers to.

   Timothy grabbed the banana and threw it in the bin.

10. Circle the verb and its tense.

    He saw his hat behind the bin.

    past   present   future

11. Circle the correct verb.

    Timothy **showed/showing** *Mrs Greene.*

12. Add speech marks to show direct speech.

    Mrs Greene said, I'm glad you found your hat, but please take it home for a wash.

MY SCORE

WEEK 9

Verb Groups and Tense

A **verb** is a word which shows actions, or states of being or having.

*We **ran** to the train station.*

(action)

*Sarah **is** the best football player.*

(being)

*We **have** a new teacher for music.*

(having)

The **tense** of the verb tells when it happens: the past, present or future.

Often an ending like s, ing or ed is added to the end of a verb to change its tense.

*My sister **helps** me make dinner.* (present)
*She **helped** me.* (past)

Sometimes, the whole verb changes to show tense or to match the person performing the verb.

*I **go*** (present)
*He **goes*** (present)
*We **went*** (past)

Some verbs use a helping verb like am, are, is, was and were to show their tense.

These are called **verb groups**.

She [**was playing**] . (past)
They [**are playing**] . (present)
We [**will play**] . (future)

Verb groups and endings often work together to show the tense.

Practice Questions

1. Circle the verb group.

   Jamie is going to the cinema tomorrow.

2. Circle the verb group that is in the future tense.

   He has invited his best friend who will meet him at the cinema.

1. Circle the verb group.

   The tall trees were growing on cliffs close to the sea.

2. Circle the verb group which is in the past tense.

   They will grow.

   They have grown.

   They are growing.

3. Circle and rewrite the misspelt word.

   The elecktrical machine broke down.

4. Write the plurals of **foot** and **mouse**.

5. Which letter is replaced by an apostrophe in the word **weren't** ?

6. Add **ing** to **destroy**.

7. Circle a similar meaning to **break**.

   brake   destroy   stop

8. Write **past** or **passed**.

   My mum let me stay up [   ]

   my bedtime to see the programme.

9. Use **bad** or **badly** in this sentence.

   He scored [   ] *in his test.*

10. Circle two verbs.

    I found a torch and turned it on.

11. Circle two adjectives.

    I had many wonderful dreams last night.

12. Add speech marks to show direct speech.

    Mum yelled, Turn out the light and go to sleep!

MY SCORE

Day 2

1. Circle the verb group.

   I am getting singing lessons every week.

2. Which verb group is in the present tense? Circle it.

   The lady who is teaching me had sung in a band long ago.

3. Rearrange the letters to spell a word that means *an electric flash across the sky*.

   I [　　　　　　　　　] l g t h i n n i g

4. Write the plurals of **woman** and **tooth**.

   [　　　　　　] [　　　　　　]

5. In alphabetical order, circle the word after **potatoes.**

   particular   promise   perhaps

6. Add **ed** to **notice**.

   [　　　　　　　　　　　]

7. Circle an opposite of **straight**.

   curved   short   upright

8. Write **past** or **passed**.

   I [　　　　　　] the swimming pool on the way to the cinema.

9. Write the missing word. **bought/brought**

   My sister [　　　　　] *her report home.*

10. Circle two verbs.

    They looked carefully, then they picked two books.

11. Circle three adjectives.

    The comfortable reading area is new.

12. Add speech marks to show direct speech.

    Peter said, What's black and white and red all over?

MY SCORE

Day 3

1. Circle the verb group.
   Hint: There are three words in this verb group.

   I have been sitting in the park.

2. Circle the verb group which is in the present tense.

   They are playing.
   They will play.
   They were playing.

3. Circle the errors and write them correctly.

   Allways obay library rules.

   [　　　　　] [　　　　　]

4. Write the plural of **library**.

   [　　　　　　　　　　]

5. Shorten **will** and **not**.

   [　　　　　　　　　　]

6. Add **ly** to **natural**.

   [　　　　　　　　　　]

7. Tick the word meaning '**to rule as a king or queen**'.

   reign [　] rain [　]

8. Write the correct word. **pear/pair**.

   This [　　　　　　] *is very juicy.*

9. **me** or **I**?

   Give that book to [　　　　　].

10. Circle two pronouns.

    I read a science fiction story with alien heroes in it.

11. Circle the two nouns.

    I will read this great book while I'm on holiday.

12. Write the words that need capital letters.

    My brother philip's birthday is in april.

    [　　　　　] [　　　　　]

MY SCORE

WEEK 9

Day 4

1. Circle the verb group.

   We have been waiting for a long time.

2. Which verb group is in the past tense? Circle it.

   After we have seen the doctor, we will go to the shop.

3. Rearrange the letters to spell a word meaning *a place for living.*

   e [   ] e v r n i e n t m o n

4. Write the incorrect plural correctly.

   foxes   potatoes   churchs

5. In alphabetical order, circle the word after *spaghetti.*

   special   separate   spade

6. Add *ly* to *gentle*.

7. Tick the correct definition of *maximum*.

   • largest amount ☐

   • a really great mother ☐

8. Circle the correct word.

   *The car drove **past/passed** us.*

9. Use *complete* or *completely* in this sentence.

   Dad needs to [   ] *empty the car.*

10. Add the missing pronoun.

   We need to replace Dad's car because [   ] *is old.*

11. Circle the two nouns.

   We both liked the car with a sunroof the best.

12. How many capital letters are missing? [   ]

   dad's favourite magazine is automobile.

MY SCORE

Day 5

1. Circle the verb group.

   We will be going on an excursion to the zoo.

2. Circle the verb group which is in the past tense.

   We have been there.
   We are going there.
   We will go there.

3. Circle the errors and write them correctly.

   She's delited with her ise cream.

4. Write the singular of each word.

   sheep [   ]   scissors [   ]

5. Shorten *could* and *not*.

6. Add *ly* to *honest*.

7. Tick the correct meaning of *misbehave*.

   • bad behaviour ☐

   • to have the wrong answer ☐

8. Circle the correct words.

   *A brave **night/knight** rode off alone into the **night/knight**.*

9. Write the correct word. **breath/breathe**

   The horse's hot [   ] *could be seen in the cold air.*

10. Add the missing pronoun.

   The brave knights swung their swords in the air as [   ] *galloped off.*

11. Circle the two nouns.

   They swiftly rode their horses to the castle.

12. Add speech marks to show direct speech.

   He proudly reported, Victory is ours, Your Majesty.

MY SCORE

New Wave English in Practice   Book 4   978-1-80087-418-3   28   Prim-Ed Publishing – www.prim-ed.com

Who is the Owner?

Granny's bag

The man's hat

My mum's computer

Who do each of these items belong to?

The apostrophe before the 's' gives us a clue. Its 'tail' points to the owner.

An apostrophe and the letter s are used when we want to show that something belongs to one person or thing.

It is never used to show a plural noun.

✔ two tigers   ✗ ~~two tiger's~~

Practice Questions

1. Use an apostrophe to shorten the words in bold.

   The **mum who belongs to the boy** was angry with him.

2. Circle the word that needs an **'s**.

   He had deliberately broken his brother new toy.

1. Use an apostrophe to shorten the part in bold.

   The **tail belonging to the cat** was sore.

2. Circle the word that needs an **'s**.

   My nan favourite food is cabbage.

3. Circle the errors and write them correctly.

   Cach it and throo it back.

4. Which word does not end with **es** in its plural?

   copy   coffee   piano

5. Shorten **they** and **will**.

6. Add **ly** to **usual**.

7. Circle an opposite of **remember**.

   memory   rejoin   forget

8. Tick the meaning of the word **minimum**.

   • a very small mother ☐

   • the lowest possible amount ☐

9. Use **happy** or **happily** in this sentence.

   The foal ⬜ trotted after its mother.

10. Circle the verb group.

    The instructor is meeting us at the stables.

11. The underlined verb group is **past/present/future** tense.

    She let me use her saddle because I had forgotten mine.

12. Add speech marks to show direct speech.

    I yelled, Come on, I'll race you to the stables.

MY SCORE

Day 2

1. Who does the **house** belong to? [   ]

   I like going to Ben's house.

2. Which word needs the apostrophe?

   [   ]

   My best friends brother is at college.

3. Rearrange the letters to spell a word meaning **surprised.**

   [a   ] a a m e z d

4. Write the singular of each word.

   mice [   ]

   gentlemen [   ]

5. In alphabetical order, which of the three words comes after **knowledge**?

   known   knock   kneel

6. Add **bi** to **sect** to make a word which means '**to cut something in two**'.

   [   ]

7. Circle the correct meaning of **brochure**.

   a radio message   a small booklet

8. Circle the correct words.

   *This **plain/plane** flies when the **weather/whether** is fine.*

9. Write **did** or **done**.

   The plane [   ] *a loop in the air.*

10. Circle two nouns.

    A light aircraft can land on a shorter runway.

11. The pronoun **it** refers to [   ].

    Leave your seat belt on, but it doesn't need to be tight.

12. Add punctuation.

    Oh, no What's that

MY SCORE [   ]

Day 3

1. Use an apostrophe to shorten the part in bold.

   *The **hens belonging to the farmer** are young.*

   [   ]

2. Circle the word that needs an **'s**.

   We collect the hen eggs every morning.

3. Circle the errors. Write them correctly.

   We wrot the rong address.

   [   ] [   ]

4. Which word doesn't have **es** in its plural form?

   box   biscuit   atlas   watch

5. Which word means **he will**?

   heal   he'll   heel

6. Add **ous** to **fame**.

   [   ]

7. Circle an opposite of **strength**.

   strangeness   weakness   energy

8. Does this sentence make sense?

   yes [   ]   no [   ]

   I occasionally go there every day.

9. Use **good** or **well** in this sentence.

   We played [   ] *and won the game.*

10. Circle the verb group.

    I will score a goal before the end of the match.

11. Change the verb to the future tense.

    The referee blew his whistle loudly.

    [   ]

12. Add speech marks.

    Why didn't you pass the ball to me? Ben shouted.

MY SCORE [   ]

Day 4

1. Who does the pencil belong to? [____]

   Ella is using Liam's pencil.

2. Which word needs the apostrophe?

   The girls books were in her school bag.

   [____]

3. Rearrange the letters to spell the **name of a gas**.

   [o ____]   o g x y n e

4. Write the plural of **disability**.

   [____]

5. In alphabetical order, which of the three words comes before **often**?

   ordinary   occasion   opposite

6. Add **bi** to **monthly** to make a word which means 'every second month'.

   [____]

7. Circle a similar meaning to **enlarge**.

   reduce   increase   complete

8. Write the correct word. **mane/main**

   What is the [____] *idea of the story?*

9. **me** or **I**?
   Hint: remove 'Dad and'. Which word makes sense?

   She smiled at Dad and [____].

10. Circle the two nouns.

    The unfortunate creature had been struck by a car.

11. What does the pronoun **it** refer to? [____]

    The vet who treated their dog said it would get better.

12. Write the words that need capital letters.

    mr tan, the vet, works in durban.

    [____]

    MY SCORE

Day 5

1. Use an apostrophe to shorten the part in bold.

   *The **howl belonging to wind** was loud and fierce.*

   [____]

2. Which word needs an **'s**?

   The man hat blew away in the wind.

   [____]

3. Circle the errors. Write them correctly.

   I herd a noize outside.

   [____]   [____]

4. Which plural word form doesn't end with **es**?

   assembly   turkey   ability

5. The shortened word **he's** can be made from **he** and **has** or from **he** and

   is   will   [____].

6. Add **ous** to **danger**.

   [____]

7. Circle an opposite of **peculiar**.

   ordinary   strange   unusual

8. Tick the meaning of the word **outrageous**.

   • something shocking and annoying [ ]

   • something expected and acceptable [ ]

9. Use **angry** or **angrily** in this sentence.

   A fisherman clambered [____] *out of his boat.*

10. Circle the verb group.

    A small fishing fleet had departed at dawn.

11. The underlined verb is **past/present/future** tense.

    He <u>saw</u> the wave just before it hit the boat.

12. Add speech marks to show direct speech.

    What kind of fish is this one? Jonathan asked.

    [____]

    MY SCORE

Adverbs

An **adverb** is a word that describes a verb.

They can change the meaning of the verb by telling how, when and how often it happens.

This makes the meaning of the verb clearer and more interesting.

*Marko **wears** his school uniform **proudly**.*
    (verb)   (adverb: how)

***Recently**, he was **made** school captain.*
(adverb: when)   (verb)

*Marko **constantly follows** the school rules.*
        (adverb: how often) (verb)

Many adverbs end in ly.

constantly   finally   neatly   calmly   quickly   exactly

We can change an adjective that describes a noun into an adverb that describes how a verb is done by adding ly.

*Marko's sister was a **beautiful** singer.*
                    (adjective)

*She sang **beautifully**.*
        (adverb)

Practice Questions

1. Circle the adverb.

   We can still be on time if we run quickly.

2. Write the verb that is described by the adverb.

   We had finally arrived at school.

1. Circle the adverb.

   The soldier fought bravely in the battle.

2. Write the verb that is described by the adverb.

   He would be rewarded eventually.

3. Circle the errors and write them correctly.

   I quiet like chocalate.

4. Write the plurals of **match** and **church**.

5. Add **in** to **active**.

6. Add **ing** to **limit**.

7. What is an opposite of **everything?**

   nothing   anything   something

8. Tick the meaning of the word **dairy**.

   • a book in which events are recorded ☐

   • a place where cows are milked ☐

9. **seen** or **saw**?

   They _____ that play last week.

10. Circle the verb group.

    Lots of children have been enjoying that play.

11. Pick the correct adjective.

    *The (**fair, guilty**) judge made the right decision.*

12. Put the apostrophe where it needs to go.

    Sams cup fell onto the floor.

MY SCORE

Day 2

1. Circle the adverb.

   The cat watched the dog suspiciously.

2. Write the verb that is described by the adverb.

   The dog would frequently chase the cat.

3. Rearrange the letters to spell a word that is a **number**.

   f [ ]   f y r o t

4. Circle the incorrect plural.

   boxes   mixes   lunchs   dishes   potatoes

5. Add two letters to **credible** to make its opposite.

6. Add **ed** to **prefer**.

7. Write the correct word.

   *What a **great/grate** day for a picnic.*

8. Which word is third in alphabetical order?

   where   which   when   who

9. **who** or **that**?
   Hint: who = person, that = thing.

   The picnic basket [ ] *I left on the rug has disappeared.*

10. Circle two verb groups.

    Our basket was taken by one of the boys who were playing near here.

11. Circle the word that needs an apostrophe.

    The boys behaviour has ruined our day.

12. Add punctuation.

    Why didn't you put the picnic basket somewhere safer Mum asked

MY SCORE

Day 3

1. Circle the adverb.

   The little girl cried sadly when she heard her pet bird was lost.

2. Write the verb that is described by the adverb.

   She would look for the bird tomorrow.

3. Circle and rewrite the misspelt word.

   She always says how pritty my sister is.

4. Write the incorrect plural correctly.

   centuries   monkies   ladies

5. Do I add **in** or **un** to **necessary** to make its opposite? [ ]

6. Add **en** to **forgot**. [ ]

7. Write the correct word. [ ]

   *Light a fire in the **great/grate** and warm up the room.*

8. Circle the correct meaning of **vacation**.

   empty   holiday

9. **who** or **that**?

   Our firewood had been cut up by the man [ ] *delivered it to the house.*

10. Circle two verb groups.

    I am making a fire and will need old newspapers and small twigs.

11. Circle three adjectives.

    The fire was so hot and bright, I could read my nature book without a light.

12. Add an apostrophe.

    Mikes lunch was squashed in the bottom of his school bag.

MY SCORE

Day 4

1. Circle two adverbs.

   If you sit quietly and look carefully, you might see the fox.

2. Write the verb that is described by the adverb.

   It usually drinks from this stream.

   [   ]

3. Rearrange the letters to spell a word meaning to **admit to doing something**.

   [c   ] c s s f e o n

4. Circle the word that doesn't end with **es** in its plural form.

   box   tomato   kangaroo   bunch

5. Circle the word with the letter **y** in its plural form.

   comedy   dictionary   driveway

6. Add **ly** to **earth**, **separate** and **particular**.

   [   ] [   ]

   [   ]

7. Circle the correct words.

   *Are you **shore/sure** we're on the **right/write** road?*

8. Which word is third in alphabetical order?

   weather   whether   what   weigh

9. **me** or **I**?

   Is that for [   ] ?

10. Circle the verb group.

    We have been driving since early morning.

11. Add an apostrophe where it is needed.

    Dads classical music tracks made me sleepy.

12. Add punctuation.

    Look at that my little sister yelled

Day 5

1. Circle two adverbs.

   He strode up to the king boldly and bowed politely.

2. Write the two verbs (verb group) that are described by the adverb.

   The knight had won a battle earlier.

   [   ] [   ]

3. Circle the error and write it correctly.

   Put it in the cuboard.

   [   ]

4. Circle the word which has no singular form.

   mice   scissors   feet

5. Does **in**, in the words **incomplete** and **incorrect**, mean in or not?

   [   ]

6. Add **er** to **garden**.

   [   ]

7. Write the word with a similar meaning to **whole**.

   hole   complete   part

   [   ]

8. Tick the meaning of the word **loose**.

   • something that isn't tight [ ]

   • to not be able to find something [ ]

9. **was** or **were**?

   That boy [   ] *crying.*

10. Circle the verb group.

    He had fallen off the slide in the park.

11. Pick the correct adjective.

    *The injured, (**distressed/ecstatic**) boy looked around for his dad.*

12. Put the apostrophe where it needs to go.

    The boys dad immediately helped him.

MY SCORE

MY SCORE

How are Commas Used?

Commas are useful punctuation marks.

They help separate words or groups of words in a sentence to help make the meaning clear.

Here are two ways that commas can be used.

Commas to separate items in lists:

A comma is placed between every word or group of words in the list except the last two.

The word **and** or **or** goes between the last two items.

You may play <u>cricket</u> , <u>tennis</u> , <u>football</u> or <u>badminton</u> in sport today.

The puppy <u>jumped free</u> , <u>sniffed his bed</u> and <u>pounced on the cat</u>.

Commas after an introduction:

A comma is placed after the group of words that introduce the sentence.

<u>After the maths test</u> , everyone let out a sigh of relief.

<u>During the holidays</u> , some children went away with their families.

Practice Questions

1. Use a comma to separate the items in the list.

   Anna Rose Elliot and Flynn were not at school today.

2. Add a comma after the introduction.

   Later that day we heard that they were all unwell.

---

1. Add commas.

   I have books pens pencils and crayons on my desk.

2. Add a comma.

   After school I go to swimming lessons.

3. Circle the spelling errors. Write them correctly.

   We'll arive in the countrey soon.

   [ ] [ ]

4. Write the only word which has a singular form.

   trousers   spectacles   women

   [ ]

5. Add **ly** to **natural, usual** and **special**.

   [ ] [ ]

   [ ]

6. Circle the correct meaning of **quite**.

   fairly   silent

7. **good** or **well**?

   The children behaved [ ] *at the beach today.*

8. Circle the correct word.

   *Mum stood on the **shore/sure** watching us swim.*

9. Is **playfully** an adverb?

   yes [ ]   no [ ]

   *The dolphins swim **playfully** in the ocean.*

10. Circle the pronoun.

    I think the island looks very interesting.

11. Add an apostrophe where it is needed.

    I can see the sails on Dans boat and his flags too.

12. Add two punctuation marks.

    When I reach the island, Ill need to have a rest

MY SCORE

Day 2

1. Add a comma.

   My chores are to feed the dog empty the dishwasher and take out the rubbish.

2. Add a comma.

   If I finish quicky I can watch my favourite shows.

3. Rearrange the letters to spell a word meaning **something awful**.

   [t   ]   t r r e b e l i

4. Shorten **who** and **has**.

   [   ]

5. Use **in** or **im** to make **possible** its opposite.

   [   ]

6. The opposite of **show** is

   hide   demonstrate   discourage

   [   ].

7. **loose** or **lose**?

   My front tooth is [   ].

8. Tick the correct sentence.

   • Mum, Julie and me went shopping. ☐

   • She bought Julie and me new shoes. ☐

9. Circle the verb that the adverb **carefully** describes.

   The little girl walked carefully in her new shoes.

10. Circle the most suitable verb.

    *Julie (**said, complained, whispered**) that her shoes were uncomfortable.*

11. Tick the sentence with the correct apostrophe.

    • Julies shoe's are red. ☐

    • Julie's shoes are red. ☐

12. How many words need capital letters? [   ]

    next thursday we'll be in boston, shopping for new clothes.

MY SCORE

Day 3

1. Add commas.

   We saw a cow pigs sheep and chickens at the farm.

2. Add a comma.

   Before feeding the animals we washed our hands.

3. Circle and rewrite the misspelt word.

   Did you notise I've cut my hair?

   [   ]

4. Write the plurals of **fish**, **cod** and **trout**.

   [   ] [   ] [   ]

5. Add **ly** to **happy** and **busy**.

   [   ] [   ]

6. Tick the meaning of the word **decline**.

   • to refuse ☐

   • to go downwards ☐

7. **loose** or **lose**?

   Did you [   ] *that tooth last night?*

8. Tick the correct sentence.

   • Liam and I think the new football coach is great. ☐

   • Other boys told Liam and I they think he's mean. ☐

9. Is **rudely** an adverb?

   yes ☐   no ☐

   Some boys spoke rudely to the new coach.

10. Circle the pronoun and the noun it refers to.

    The new coach said he would speak to the boys after football practice.

11. Who does the car belong to? [   ]

    The boys met the coach by his car.

12. How many words need capital letters? [   ]

    they want mr walsh, the coach, to go back to his football team in perth as soon as possible.

MY SCORE

Day 4

1. Add commas.

   Roses tulips daffodils and lavender grow well in the beautiful garden.

2. Add a comma.

   During spring the garden is filled with butterflies and bees.

3. Rearrange the letters to spell a word meaning to **keep going**.

   | c | | c n o u t i e n

4. **Who's** can be shortened from **who** and **has** or

   who and [ ].

5. Add **in** or **im** to **patient** to make its opposite.

   [ ]

6. The opposite of **definite** is

   clear   uncertain   exact

   [ ].

7. **good** or **well**?

   The injured patient is walking [ ] *again.*

8. Which word is last in alphabetical order?

   laugh   letter   loose   lesson

   [ ]

9. Circle the verb that the adverb **quickly** describes.

   The ambulance drove to the hospital quickly.

10. Circle the better verb for **said** in this sentence.

    *The doctor (**announced, demanded**) that the boy would need to stay a few days longer.*

11. Add an apostrophe where it is needed.

    The boys mum brought him some books to read while he recovered.

12. Add speech marks for direct speech.

    Please can I get out of bed today and have a shower? pleaded the poor boy.

Day 5

1. Add commas.

   'Would you like to read a book do a drawing or rest?' asked my grandma.

2. Add a comma.

   'When I feel better I would like to draw', I replied.

3. Circle the spelling errors. Write them correctly.

   Our gardiner planted froot trees.

   [ ]   [ ]

4. Write the singular form of **clippers** and **tongs**.

   [ ]   [ ]

5. Add **ly** to **funny** and **noisy**.

   [ ]   [ ]

6. Tick the meaning of the word **antiseptic**.

   • a chemical used to kill germs   [ ]

   • a substance used to stop sweating   [ ]

7. **good** or **well**?

   That dog is trained [ ].

8. Which word is first in alphabetical order?

   dear   decorate   decision   declare

   [ ]

9. Is **patiently** an adverb?

   yes [ ]   no [ ]

   *The dog stops and waits **patiently** until the traffic has gone.*

10. Circle the better verb for **said** in this sentence.

    *'Let's go, boy!', (**commanded, begged**) its owner.*

11. Add an apostrophe where it is needed.

    The mans lovely dog is always very obedient.

12. Add speech marks for direct speech.

    Did you train this dog yourself? I asked.

WEEK 13

Joining Two Independent Ideas

A simple sentence is a group of words that form a complete idea.

They make sense on their own.

Simple sentences have a naming part and a telling part.

The dog played fetch with its owner.

(naming part)   (telling part)

Often, simple sentences are joined together to make a longer sentence.

This is done using a conjunction like **and, or, so** or **but**.

The dog played fetch with its owner, so *it was very tired.*

They went to the park, and *they played a game of fetch.*

The owner was ready to go home, but *the dog still wanted to play.*

They could go home, or *they could stay at the park.*

Joining two simple sentences helps make your writing more interesting.

Practice Questions

1. Circle the joining word (conjunction).

   I wanted to go for a bike ride, but then it began to rain.

2. Add the conjunction (joining word) **or** or **so**.

   Ben couldn't decide whether to play football [____] cricket.

1. Circle the joining word (conjunction).

   We cut the cake and then we put a slice on each plate.

2. Add the conjunction (joining word) **or** or **so**.

   We offered everyone a piece, [____] we ran out of cake quickly.

3. Circle and rewrite the misspelt words.

   My favoreet aunt gose to France every summer.

   [____] [____]

4. Which word has no singular form?

   scissors   businesses   gentlemen

   [____]

5. Add **er** to **begin**.

   [____]

6. Circle the correct words.

   *He **mist/missed** his bus so he didn't **meat/meet** me.*

7. Shorten **we** and **have**.

   [____]

8. **who** or **which**?
   Hint: who = person, which = thing.

   The lady [____] made the cake is Mum's friend.

9. **a** or **an**?
   Hint: use **an** before a vowel or vowel sound.

   She told us the cake took [____] hour to bake.

10. The underlined word is an [____].

    adjective   adverb

    The chef skilfully added tasty icing to the cake.

11. Add an apostrophe.

    The ladys cakes are always delicious.

12. How many words need capital letters? [____]

    mrs murphy used an old irish cake recipe her mother taught her.

    MY SCORE

Day 2

1. Circle the joining word (conjunction).

   I walk to school, but I catch a bus when it rains.

2. Add the conjunction (joining word) **but** or **so**.

   I missed the bus, [____] *I had to walk.*

3. Rearrange the letters to spell a word meaning **a place where books can be borrowed**.

   [l _____] l b r i a y r

4. Which word is the opposite of **believable**?

   inbelievable   unbelievable   onbelievable

   [_____]

5. Add **ing** to **occur**.

   [_____]

6. An opposite of **nothing** is [_____].

   anybody   anything   something

7. Which word is second in alphabetical order?

   object   occasion   ocean   occur

   [_____]

8. **who** or **that**?

   The girl will sit at a desk [_____] *is near mine.*

9. **a** or **an**?

   The new girl already has her uniform, but she will need to buy [_____] *art folder.*

10. Cross out the word that is not needed.

    Our school is great and all the children like it they're.

11. Add a comma.

    Before she starts she will need a tie with the school badge on it.

12. Add speech marks.

    She asked, Will I need to buy a sports jersey too?

    MY SCORE

Day 3

1. Circle the joining word (conjunction).

   I lost my hat and I couldn't find my shoes.

2. Add the conjunction (joining word) **but** or **so**.

   I looked and looked [_____] *I still couldn't find them.*

3. Circle the spelling errors and write them correctly.

   I offen visit this iland.

   [_____]   [_____]

4. Circle the word that is always written in a plural form.

   wives   pyjamas   humans

5. Add **ed** to **admit**.

   [_____]

6. Circle the correct words.

   To/Two/Too *of the boys are* **to/two/too** *tired* **to/two/too** *play with us.*

7. Shorten **how** and **will**.

   [_____]

8. **did** or **done**?

   My friend [_____] *her homework on the bus.*

9. Tick the meaning of the word **appoint**.

   • to choose a person to do something [ ]

   • to send someone in a certain direction [ ]

10. The underlined word is an [_____].

    adjective   adverb

    We were all talking <u>loudly</u> *to each other on the bus.*

11. Add an apostrophe.

    This mans shoes are black and shiny.

12. How many words need capital letters? [_____]

    saint valentine's day is in february.

    MY SCORE

Day 4

1. Circle the joining word (conjunction).

   We waited under the tree, but the rain didn't stop.

2. Add the conjunction (joining word) *or* or *but*.

   Hopefully the rain will stop soon, [ ] *we will be late.*

3. Rearrange the letters to spell a word meaning *an instrument*.

   [g]   g i u r a t

4. Circle the word that is the opposite of *wise*.

   inwise   onwise   unwise

5. Add *ly* to *brief* and *weird*.

   [ ]   [ ]

6. An opposite of *moist* is [ ].

   rain   dry   damp

7. Which word is last in alphabetical order?

   swelter   switch   swallow   sword

   [ ]

8. *did* or *done*?

   What have you [ ] *with my football boots?*

9. Tick the meaning of the word *aisle*.

   • a small isolated island [ ]

   • a path between seats in a hall [ ]

10. Cross out the word that is not needed.

    It is very annoying when I can't not find my things.

11. Add a comma.

    I found my lost ruler drink bottle and library book under my bed.

12. Add punctuation.

    I've found them I yelled.

MY SCORE

Day 5

1. Circle the joining word (conjunction).

   I was reading a book and Dad was washing the car.

2. Add the conjunction (joining word) *so* or *but*.

   It was getting hot outside, [ ] *I went in the house to get a drink.*

3. Circle and rewrite the misspelt word.

   When will that famous actor apear?

   [ ]

4. Which singular is correct? [ ]

   scissor   tweezer   dozen

5. Add *ly* to *unlike* and *strange*.

   [ ]   [ ]

6. Circle the correct words.

   *Tie a **not/knot** in it and make **shore/sure** it's tight.*

7. Shorten *you* and *had*.

   [ ]

8. *me* or *I*?

   The man who owned this boat was pleased with [ ].

9. *all ready* or *already*? [ ]

   *The boats are **all ready/already** to go out.*

10. Write the adverb. [ ]

    The boys were fishing contently.

11. Add commas.

    I will need to take a hat suncream a drink and something to eat on the boat.

12. Add a comma.

    Although it was raining we kept fishing.

MY SCORE

Nouns That Name a Feeling

Some nouns are words that name things we can't touch, smell, see, taste or hear.

They are often the names of feelings, events and ideas.

These types of nouns are called **abstract nouns**.

Some examples of abstract nouns include:

anger, beauty, confidence, freedom, fun, health, help, love, luck, peace, sleep, time, wealth.

Endings are often added to the end of verbs, adjectives and other nouns to make them into abstract nouns.

For example:

happy + ness = happiness
(adjective)   (abstract noun)

inform + tion = information
(verb)   (abstract noun)

friend + ship = friendship
(noun)   (abstract noun)

Practice Questions

1. Circle the noun that names a feeling.

   There was fear in his eyes.

2. Write the noun that does not name a feeling.

   [   ]

disgust   excitement   person

1. Circle the noun that names a feeling.

   That firefighter showed great bravery when he rescued the man.

2. Circle the noun that does not name a feeling.

   fear   despair   bravery   ladder

3. Circle and rewrite the misspelt word.

   We bawt a new car.

   [   ]

4. Add **ly** to **personal**.

   [   ]

5. Add **il** to **legal**.

   [   ]

6. Shorten **you** and **are**.

   [   ]

7. Circle the correct words.

   Your injured **heel/heal** *looks very* **sore/saw**.

8. **all ready** or **already**?

   [   ]

   I've **all ready/already** *put an ice pack on it.*

9. **me** or **I**?

   Mum and [   ] *had an appointment to see a doctor.*

10. Circle the conjunction (joining word).

    The doctor told me I couldn't swim and he checked my injury again.

11. Rewrite this phrase using an apostrophe.

    the advice belonging to the doctor

    [   ]

12. Add a comma.

    When I'm allowed to swim again I'll train very hard every day.

MY SCORE

Day 2

1. Circle the noun that names a feeling.

   You could see the delight on the children's faces.

2. Circle the noun that names a feeling.

   cinema   excitement   popcorn   audience

3. Rearrange the letters to spell a word meaning something **unknown**.

   [m   ] m t e r y s y

4. Add **ly** to **final** and **mental**.

   [   ] [   ]

5. A similar meaning to **skilful** is [   ].

   awkward   talented   clumsy

6. Which word is last in alphabetical order?

   thorn   throw   thrash

7. Tick the meaning of the word **whimper**.

   • to bark   ☐

   • to cry weakly   ☐

8. **lend** or **borrow**?

   I will [   ] *you my favourite book.*

9. Circle two verbs.

   Please return my book before you go home.

10. Circle the conjunction (joining word).

    You can read the book about dragons or you can read the book about dinosaurs.

11. Rewrite this phrase using an apostrophe.

    the rules belonging to our school

    [   ]

12. Add an apostrophe.

    When I saw my friends car I was amazed.

Day 3

1. Circle the noun that names a feeling.

   Spending time with my family brings me happiness.

2. Circle the noun that does not name a feeling.

   delight   amusement   family   happiness

3. Circle the errors and write them correctly.

   Fish can breath underwarter.

   [   ] [   ]

4. Add **ly** to **lucky** and **easy**.

   [   ] [   ]

5. Which word is the opposite of **believable**?

   inbelievable   unbelievable   onbelievable

6. **Didn't** is shortened from [   ] and

   [   ].

7. Tick the meaning of the word **thrive**.

   • to do well   ☐

   • to force or push hard   ☐

8. **lend** or **lenf**?

   Where is the beach towel I [   ] *you?*

9. Write the correct verb.

   She always **wear/wears** *suncream and a sun hat.*

10. Circle the conjunction (joining word).

    I can go to the cinema, but I need to finish all my homework first.

11. Rewrite this phrase using an apostrophe.

    a ball belonging to Tom

    [   ]

12. Add an apostrophe.

    The ladys umbrella was blown into the ocean by some very strong winds.

Day 4

1. Circle the noun that names an idea.

   Our friendship means a lot to me.

2. Circle the noun that names a feeling.

   love   friend   gift

3. Rearrange the letters to spell a word meaning something for **cutting**.

   [s   ] s s s s i c r o

4. Add **ly** to **helpful**.

   [   ]

5. An opposite of **accurate** is [   ].

   careless   quiet   precise

6. Which word is after **whisper** in alphabetical order?

   whisker   whistle   whimper

7. Circle the correct words.

   I heard **your/you're** *loud* **groan/grown**.

8. **All together** or **Altogether**?

   [   ]*, there are 20 teeth in a child's mouth.*

9. Tick the correct sentence.

   • The dentist gave Ben and I a sticker. ☐

   • Ben and I both felt very proud. ☐

10. Circle the conjunction (joining word).

    I want to go, but it is too late.

11. Tick the sentence with the correct apostrophe.

    • Bens' sticker is bigger. ☐

    • Ben's sticker is bigger. ☐

12. Are the two commas in the correct places?

    yes ☐   no ☐

    I bought cheese, onions, and tomatoes in the supermarket.

Day 5

1. Circle the noun that names a feeling.

   Dad's beautiful garden filled him with pride.

2. Circle the noun that names a feeling.

   petunias   gloves   enjoyment

3. Circle and rewrite the misspelt word.

   What materiel was used in construction?

   [   ]

4. Add **ly** to **wonderful**.

   [   ]

5. Add **il** to **literate**.

   [   ]

6. **We're** is shortened from [   ] and [   ].

7. Circle the correct words.

   You're/Your *plants have* **grown/groan** *so tall.*

8. **all together** or **altogether**?

   Did you separate the coloured petunias or did you plant them [   ]*?*

9. Tick the correct sentence.

   • Dad and I enjoy gardening. ☐

   • Mum bought Dad and I gloves. ☐

10. Circle the conjunction (joining word).

    My gardening gloves are too small, so Mum lent me her gloves.

11. Tick the sentence with the correct apostrophe.

    • Dad's gloves are red. ☐

    • Dads' gloves are red. ☐

12. Add commas.

    I mowed the lawn collected the weeds swept the leaves and then had a long rest.

Types of Sentences

There are four types of sentences that are used in writing. Each sentence has a different purpose.

Let's learn more about each of these.

> Jellyfish have no heart or brain.

This sentence is a statement. It is used to share an idea, fact or opinion. Statements end with a full stop.

> Put your toys away.

This sentence is a command. It is used to give an instruction. Commands are usually very short and include a bossy verb (a verb that tells someone what to do). They end with a full stop.

> What is your favourite colour?

This sentence is a question. It is used to ask something. Questions usually end with a question mark.

> I can't believe we won!

This sentence is an exclamation. It is used to show a strong feeling like surprise or anger. Exclamations can also be a statement or command, but they end with an exclamation mark.

Practice Questions

Are these sentences a statement, a question or a command?

1. *Have you packed away your things?*

2. *My books and pencil case are in my bag.*

3. *Please finish your homework over the weekend.*

---

1. Is this a statement, a question or a command?

   Turn off the light and go to sleep.

2. Punctuate.

   'I don't want to go to bed yet [ ] ' I yelled angrily.

3. Circle the errors and write them correctly.

   Now drawer a circel for a head.

4. Add **ment** to **enjoy** to make an abstract noun.

5. Which word comes after **friend** in a dictionary?

   friction   frequent   fright

6. Tick the meaning of the word **possession**.

   • something you own [ ]

   • something you would like to own [ ]

7. **of** or **off**?

   Take your cap [ ] when you go inside.

8. Circle the noun.

   Our school is great.

9. Circle two pronouns.

   I asked what he was doing after school.

10. **his** or **if**?

    My project is finished, but he still has to do [ ] .

11. Add the missing pronouns. **he/she/it**

    Joe said [ ] had to work on his project

    tonight or [ ] wouldn't be finished.

12. Add two apostrophes.

    Ryans dad believes that childrens homework is important.

MY SCORE

Day 2

1. Is this a statement, a question or a command?

   This is the best film I've seen.

2. Punctuate.

   What is it called ☐

3. Rearrange the letters to spell a word meaning **foolish**.

   r _____ r d i l u o s i c u

4. Add **ment** to **excite** to make an abstract noun.

5. Which word comes before **work** in a dictionary?

   world   worse   wooden

6. Tick the meaning of the word **transparent**.

   • a parent who works in different places ☐

   • something you can see through ☐

7. Add **an** or **a**.

   Would you prefer ☐ *apple or* ☐ *banana?*

8. Circle the adjective and underline the noun it describes.

   I think the fruit is delicious.

9. Circle one verb and underline the adverb that tells how.

   The lightning flashed brightly in the night sky.

10. **his** or **if**?

    Adam saw ☐ *mum's comb but can't*

    remember exactly where he saw ☐ .

11. Add the missing pronouns. **they/us/we**

    Mum told ☐ *that* ☐

    should all eat more fruit.

12. Add an apostrophe.

    Bobs favourite fruit is the banana.

    MY SCORE ☐

Day 3

1. Is this a statement, a question or a command?

   Is this your favourite book?

2. Punctuate.

   I like reading Harry Potter books ☐

3. Correct the spelling error.

   Our travel gide showed us some exciting places.

4. Add **ness** to **foolish** to make an abstract noun.

5. Shorten **she** and **had**.

6. A similar meaning to **repair** is

   refund   renovate   refuse ☐ .

7. **tired** or **tried**?

   We ☐ *to make sure it was safe.*

8. The pronoun **them** refers to ☐ .

   She picked up her sunglasses and gave them to me.

9. Write the correct pronoun.

   I can't find my coat and hat. Do you know where

   ☐ *are?*

10. Which conjunction could join the two sentences?

    and   **but**   **so**   ☐

    Patrick loves playing tennis. He has never won a match.

11. Circle the correct one.

    My friend **picked up/put down** *her beach towel from the sand.*

12. Add a comma.

    Under her beach towel I discovered the book I'd been searching for.

    MY SCORE ☐

Day 4

1. Is it a statement, a question or a command?

   'I'm free! Kick it to me!' he bellowed.

2. Punctuate.

   Did you see that goal ☐

3. Rearrange the letters to spell a part of the **body**.

   h _____   h r t e a

4. Add **ness** to **polite** to make an abstract noun.

5. Shorten **it** and **will**.

6. The opposite of **curly** is _____ .

   crooked   wavy   straight

7. **draw** or **drawer**?

   Put your socks in your _____ .

8. Circle two adjectives and underline the nouns they describe.

   The polite girl wrote a fantastic story for the competition.

9. Circle the verb group and underline the adverb that tells how.

   She had worked tirelessly on her submission.

10. Which conjunction could join the two sentences?

    and   **but**   **so**   _____

    Kate doesn't want to do badly in her test. She has been practising her spelling words.

11. Cross out the word that does not belong.

    The boys all played well because despite the terrible weather.

12. Add a comma.

    After the game they all enjoyed a hamburger.

Day 5

1. Is this a statement, a question or a command?

   My cat just had five kittens.

2. Punctuate.

   Taking care of kittens is a lot of work ☐

3. Circle the error and write it correctly.

   The diver took a deep breathe. _____

4. Add **ness** to **kind** to make an abstract noun.

5. Circle the first word in alphabetical order.

   overhead   overtake   overlap   overdose

6. Tick the meaning of the word **herd**.

   • a group of the same animals ☐
   • something you have listened to ☐

7. Add the verb **is, am** or **are**.

   My friends and I _____ *having a picnic.*

8. Circle the nouns.

   The storm destroyed the tree.

9. Circle the verb group and underline the adverb that tells how.

   It was raining heavily.

10. Which conjunction could join the two sentences?

    and   **but**   **so**   _____

    Dad wanted to go to the cinema. Mum asked if she could come too.

11. Add the missing pronoun. **Us/We**

    _____ *decided to have lunch at home instead.*

12. Add an apostrophe.

    My sisters friend stayed and we all had an enjoyable lunch together.

MY SCORE   MY SCORE

Day 1

1. Circle the error and write it correctly.

   My apointment is at eight.

2. Add *ation* to *consider* and *inform* to make the abstract nouns.

3. Add *es* to the verb *cry*.

   The lost boy _____ *for his mum.*

4. Circle the last word in alphabetical order.

   grumpy   grubby   gruesome

5. Tick the meaning of the word *gruesome*.

   • the way something grows ☐

   • something causing feelings of horror ☐

6. Add the verb *is, am* or *are*.

   I _____ *sorry that you weren't home today.*

7. Circle the verb group.

   We are going to the cinema.

8. Circle the conjunction (joining word).

   I can't go, but I will let you know if things change.

9. Write the correct verb.

   *Taj and I **used to go/went** to the cinema at weekends.*

10. Cross out the word that does not belong.

    Would not you like to come with us next time?

11. Is this a statement, a question or a command?

    Put your shoes on and let's go.

12. Add a comma.

    Before we see the film I will need to buy our tickets.

MY SCORE

Day 2

1. Rearrange the letters to spell a word that means *something placed on a window*.

   c _____ t u r c n i a

2. Write two of these words in their plural form.

   The wife picked up the knife.

3. The opposite of *famous* is _____ .

   favourite   unknown   fantastic

4. Shorten *he* and *has*.

5. Circle the correct word.

   *Don't **meddle/medal** in other people's business.*

6. *lend* or *borrow*?

   May I please _____ *your tennis racquet?*

7. Circle two verb groups in this sentence.

   If you will be careful, I will lend it to you.

8. Circle the conjunction (joining word).

   I'll get it today, so I won't need to rush around tomorrow.

9. Cross out the word that does not belong.

   I will return your tennis racquet net after the match.

10. Does this sentence make sense?

    yes ☐   no ☐

    I could see through the transparent stone wall.

11. Is this a statement, a question or a command?

    I'm very pleased that you are trusting me with your expensive racquet.

12. Add punctuation.

    He looked worried and asked, You will look after it, won't you

MY SCORE

Day 3

1. Correct the spelling error.

   I enjoy competing in extreem sports.

2. Add **ation** to **admire** and **adore** to make the abstract nouns.
   Hint: drop the e.

3. Add **es** to the verb **hurry**.

   She always [____] *home.*

4. **He's** is shortened from **he** and **has** and **he** and

   [____] .

5. Circle the correct word.

   Dad won this meddle/medal for bravery.

6. **lend** or **borrow**.

   I will only [____] *this to you for one week.*

7. Circle two verb groups in this sentence.

   It is going to be a busy week, but I will try to read fast.

8. Circle the conjunction (joining word).

   Chloe wants to read that magazine, so you can read it when she is finished.

9. Cross out the word that does not belong.

   After he has read behind the magazine, I might read it.

10. Does this sentence make sense?

    yes [ ]   no [ ]

    I read very quickly, especially if it's an exciting film.

11. Is this a statement, a question or a command?

    Give the book to Chloe.

12. Add a comma.

    After school I often ride my bike to the library.

MY SCORE

Day 4

1. Rearrange the letters to spell a word that means a subject about **countries, mountains** and **rivers**.

   [g]   p a g r e g h o y

2. Write the singular of **our scissors**.

3. A close meaning to **tame** is [____] .

   wild   friendly   patient

4. Circle the first word in alphabetical order.

   locomotive   lookout   locker   lonely

5. Tick the meaning of the word **international**.

   • between or among nations [ ]

   • within a nation [ ]

6. Add the verb **has** or **have**.

   You [____] *to help your mother.*

7. Circle the verb group.

   I must wash the dishes.

8. Circle the conjunction.

   I promised I'd clean their rooms, but they have to mow the lawn.

9. Write the correct verb.

   My brothers **grumbles/grumble** *about cleaning their rooms.*

10. Cross out the word that does not belong.

    Although they hate work, they always don't mind gardening.

11. Is this a statement, a question or a command?

    'We're finished!' the boys told their dad.

12. Add punctuation.

    You did a great job, Dad commented

MY SCORE

Day 5

1. Circle the error and write it correctly.

   She rote a long letter.

2. Add *ation* to *sense* and *restore* to make the abstract nouns.

3. Add *es* to the verb *carry*.

   Dad [ ] *Mum's shopping.*

4. Circle the last word in alphabetical order.

   stimulate   stitch   stepladder

5. Tick the meaning of the word *locomotive*.

   • someone who does silly things [ ]

   • an engine that pulls railway carriages [ ]

6. Add the verb *has* or *have*.

   The train [ ] *just left the station.*

7. Circle the verb group.

   I will catch the next one.

8. Circle the conjunction (joining word).

   You wait here and I will get your coat.

9. Write the correct verb.

   *My friend and I **is/are** going to a new shopping centre.*

10. Cross out the word that does not belong.

    Before we board the train room, I'll phone and let Mum know.

11. Is this a statement, a question or a command?

    May I borrow your phone?

12. Add punctuation.

    Will you please pick us up from the station I asked.

Skill Focus Review

1. Circle the error and write it correctly.

   My mum bawt a new car.

2. Circle the word which does not have a **y** in its plural. Write its plural. [ ]

   country   relay   monkey

3. Add *ment* to *achieve* to make an abstract noun.

4. Write *past* or *passed*.

   Kevin saw a rat as he walked [ ] *the shed.*

5. *me* or *I*?

   Dad and [ ] *think red cars are nicer.*

6. Is *pride* an abstract noun (something that can't be touched)? [ ]

   Dad was filled with pride.

7. Circle the verb group.

   Dad had been wanting a new car for a long time.

8. The underlined verb group is *past/present/future* tense.

   He will collect his new car next week.

9. Circle the adverb.

   Dad drives his new car slowly.

10. Circle the joining word (conjunction).

    We arrived home and Dad was excited to show Mum his new car.

11. Use an apostrophe to shorten the part in bold.

    *Mum loves **the car belonging to Dad**.*

12. Add commas.

    Dad went to the shop to buy soap polish sponges and cloths to keep his car clean.

MY SCORE

MY SCORE

WEEK 17

Joining Two Related Ideas

A simple sentence is a group of words that form a complete idea.

They make sense on their own.

Simple sentences have a naming part and a telling part.

<u>We will play cricket this afternoon.</u>

(naming part)   (telling part)

We can make our sentences longer and more detailed using a conjunction like **before, after, if, while, unless, because, when** or **although**.

This type of conjunction joins a simple sentence with a related idea that does not make sense on its own. They can be used in the middle or at the start of a sentence. For example:

We will play cricket this afternoon **if** **it's not too hot.**

If **it's not too hot**, *we will play cricket this afternoon*.

In both sentences, the underlined words do not make sense on their own.

Each conjunction has a different purpose. For example:

- **because** is used to show the reason for the first part of the sentence.
- **unless** gives an exception to the first part of the sentence.

Do you know when to use some of the other conjunctions?

Practice Questions

1. Circle the conjunctions.

   I am not good at football, although I practise every day.

   While I practise, my mum reads a book.

2. Choose the best conjunction.

   before   unless   while

   Gran gave everyone a present [   ] she left.

---

1. Circle the conjunction.

   Try asking for help before you throw a tantrum.

2. Circle the conjunction.

   Before I help you, clean up this mess!

3. Correct the spelling error.

   My dad still has an old electrick train.

   [   ]

4. Add **ation** to **inform** to make an abstract noun.

   [   ]

5. Which noun does not have the same singular and plural form?

   sheep   trout   tooth   salmon

   [   ]

6. Circle the correct words.

   *Come **here/hear**, I think you should **here/hear** this.*

7. **it's** or **its**?

   I can't find my maths book. I think [   ] at home.

8. A similar meaning to **obvious** is

   clear   hidden   concealed

   [   ].

9. **angle** or **angel**?

   Which is the biggest [   ] in this triangle?

10. Circle two nouns.

    Maths is boring and it's not as easy as English.

11. Circle two adjectives.

    I like reading books that are mysterious and scary.

12. Add a comma.

    After I go to bed I read until Dad turns off my light.

MY SCORE

Day 2

1. Circle the conjunction.

   My uncle said I could go out fishing with him if my parents agreed.

2. Circle the conjunction.

   If we go fishing, we will be leaving very early.

3. Rearrange the letters to spell a word meaning **not the same**.

   | d |

   d f f e n t e r i

4. Add **ation** to **navigate** to make an abstract noun.

5. Only one of these nouns has a singular form.

   Write it.

   measles   tweezers   feet   scissors

6. Write the correct word. **wait/weight**

   This graph shows the [   ] *of every boy.*

7. Shorten **we** and **would**.

8. Circle the most suitable verb.

   *Buildings (**collapsed, folded, moved**) during the earthquake.*

9. **angle or angel**?

   Try to see this matter from a different

10. Circle the adjectives.

    Lisa's brother is tall and thin, but he's not a fast runner.

11. Circle the verb and the adverb that tells how.

    My athletic sister runs tirelessly.

12. How many capital letters are missing from this sentence? [   ]

    My sister, grace, hopes to be on the spanish tennis team next year and to play with them in france.

Day 3

1. Circle the conjunction.

   The cows follow each other out of the shed after the milking is finished.

2. Circle the conjunction.

   After the milk is collected, the farmers use it to make yoghurt and cheese.

3. Circle the spelling error. Write it correctly.

   His raign lasted ten years.

4. Circle the correct opposite of **honest**.

   inhonest   dishonest   antihonest

5. Circle the first word in alphabetical order.

   kidney   kilometre   kind   kidnap

6. Tick the meaning of the word **experience**.

   • something that happens to someone [ ]

   • telling someone about something [ ]

7. Circle the correct verb.

   *The lifeguard **go/goes** into the water every day.*

8. The opposite of **result** is [   ].

   outcome   effect   cause

9. Add **diary** or **dairy**.

   The cows follow each other into the

   [   ]

10. Circle three nouns
    Hint: one is abstract.

    Cows have beautiful brown eyes and a gentle nature.

11. Circle two adjectives.

    The cows in the field sheltered under the trees because it was wet and stormy.

12. Add punctuation marks.

    I yelled, Run That bull looks angry.

Day 4

1. Circle the conjunction.

   The mother hen carefully watched while her chicks wandered around the farmyard.

2. Circle the conjunction.

   While they played, a sly fox looked on hungrily.

3. Rearrange the letters to spell a word that means **different types**.

   v [   ] r a v s i o u

4. Add **re** to **load** and **grew**.

   [   ] [   ]

5. Circle the last word in alphabetical order.

   relocate   religion   reluctant   relaxation

6. Tick the meaning of the word **independent**.

   • needing help from other people ☐

   • being able to look after yourself ☐

7. Shorten **it** and **would**. [   ]

8. Circle the most suitable verb.

   *This athlete (**ran, sprinted, strolled**) down the track.*

9. Add **than** or **then**.

   You are quicker [   ] *I am.*

10. Circle the adjectives.

    Just look at the cute and playful pups!

11. Circle the verb and the adverb that tells how.

    The mother watched her puppies anxiously.

12. Add punctuation.

    Can I please have one I begged.

Day 5

1. Circle the conjunction.

   My brother likes to play football although he is always very clumsy.

2. Circle the conjunction.

   Although we are an excellent team, we have never won a match.

3. Correct the spelling error.

   Those two children are my niece and my nefew.

   [   ]

4. Add **ion** to **inject** and **invent** to make nouns.

   [   ] [   ]

5. Which word does not add **es** to form its plural?

   potato   watch   cake   class   atlas

6. Circle the correct word.

   *The **mare/mayor** gave out the awards at the town hall.*

7. Write the correct verb. [   ]

   *The busy workers **fill/fills** the boxes with food.*

8. A similar meaning to **familiar** is

   [   ].

   foreign   normal   strange

9. **guess** or **guest**?

   Can you [   ] *who my favourite actor is?*

10. Circle two nouns.

    Many famous old actors were invited to the event.

11. Circle two adjectives.

    Before he became a famous actor, he was a commercial pilot.

12. Write the words that need capital letters.

    He made films in hollywood and appeared on the stage in london.

    [   ] [   ]

Changing Base Words

Often, groups of letters are added to the beginning of words to create new words.

Each new word has a different meaning to the original **base word**.

There are many different groups of letters, and each of these has its own meaning.

Let's explore some of these below.

un- mis- dis-
meaning 'opposite'
unclean
misbehave
disapprove

re-
meaning 'again' or 'back'
replay

inter-
meaning 'between'
interact

anti-
meaning 'against'
anticlockwise

pre-
meaning 'before'
preview

bi- tri-
meaning 'two' and 'three'
bicycle
triangle

sub-
meaning 'under'
submarine

super-
meaning 'above'
supermarket

auto-
meaning 'self' or 'own'
autobiography

semi-
meaning 'half'
semicircle

in-
meaning 'not'
incomplete

- use **il** before a root word starting with l: **il**legal
- use **im** before a root word starting with m or p: **im**patient
- use **ir** before a root word starting with r: **ir**responsible

Usually, we do not need to change the base word when we add letters to its beginning.

Practice Questions

1. Draw lines to match the beginnings with their meanings.

   re   ◐ half

   pre   ⊘ against

   sub   ↻ again

   semi   ⬆ under

   anti   ◉ before

---

1. Add **semi** to **colon**.

2. The **semi** in **semicircle** means **super** or **half** ?

3. Correct the spelling error.

   An orfan is a child who hasn't got any parents.

4. Add **ion** to **hesitate** and **complete** to make nouns.

5. Which word does not change **f** to **v** in its plural?

   thief   shelf   reef   wolf   self

6. Circle the correct words.

   *The **mare/mayor** came trotting **through/threw** the stable door.*

7. Shorten **it** and **had**.

8. A similar meaning to **accidental** is

   .
   deliberate   unplanned   intentional

9. **guess** or **guesf**?

   We invited an interesting [＿＿＿] *speaker.*

10. Circle the noun.

    His intelligent, clever guide dog came with him.

11. Circle the conjunction.

    A guide dog can make a huge difference in your life if you are blind.

12. Add three missing capital letters.

    I think that guide dogs for the blind is a wonderful organisation.

MY SCORE

Day 2

1. Add **bi** to **plane**.

2. Does **bi** in the word **bicycle** mean that it has one, two or three wheels?

3. Rearrange the letters to spell a word that means **something you can see through**.

   t _____ r a s p a n t r e n t

4. Add **ir** meaning **not** to **regular** and **responsible**.

5. Which word is first in alphabetical order?

   taste   tattoo   tartan

6. Tick the meaning of the word **courage**.

   • the strength to do something frightening ☐

   • trying not to be angry ☐

7. Write the correct past tense of **catch**.
   catched/caught

8. Circle the most suitable verb.

   *The famous chef carefully (**purchased, bought, prepared**) the dessert.*

9. Add **comma** or **coma**.

   He has been in a _____ for two weeks.

10. Circle the verb group.

    The poor patient was involved in a terrible car accident.

11. Circle the conjunction.

    His family will stay by his bed until he is better.

12. Add speech marks for direct speech.

    Can you hear me, James? his mother whispered.

MY SCORE

Day 3

1. Add **pre** to **mix** and **heat**.

2. The **pre** in **precook** and **premade** means **before** or **beside**?

3. Circle the spelling error. Write it correctly.

   We will serch until we find him.

4. Circle the correct opposite of **steady**.

   unsteady   insteady   ansteady

5. Circle the second in alphabetical order.

   disabled   disaster   discard   disbelief

6. Tick the meaning of the word **hibernation**.

   • a doctor who does surgery ☐

   • to sleep through the winter ☐

7. Shorten **they** and **are**.

8. The opposite of ridiculous is _____.

   foolish   wise   senseless

9. Add **comma** or **coma**.

   A _____ is used in a sentence.

10. Circle the verb group.

    These athletes have been training hard all year.

11. Cross out the word that does not belong.

    Just unless something unexpected happens, they should be playing in the finals.

12. How many capital letters are missing?

    South africa are playing australia at rugby next saturday.

MY SCORE

Day 4

1. Add *tri* to *angle*.

2. Does *tri* in the word *tricycle* mean that it has one, two or three wheels?

3. Rearrange the letters to spell a *fraction*.

q [   ] q r t u a r e

4. Add *ion* to *express* and *discuss*.

5. Circle the incorrect plural.

lunches   torches   stomaches   patches

6. Circle the correct words.

The jockey held onto the **reins/rains/reigns** tightly as **rein/rain/reign** fell on the muddy track.

7. Is *goes* or *went* the past tense of *go*?

8. Circle the better verb for *said* in this sentence.

'The baby has just fallen asleep', (**announced, whispered**) Mum.

9. *goal* or *gaol* ?

His [   ] was to win as many races as possible.

10. Circle the verb and the adverb that tells when.

That horse raced brilliantly yesterday.

11. Circle the conjunction.

The trainer was worried because his horse ran better on a dry track.

12. Write with punctuation.

come on, you can do it I yelled

MY SCORE

Day 5

1. Add *anti* to *climax*.

2. The *anti* in *antiseptic* and *antisocial* means *against* or *agree*?

3. Correct the spelling error.

Don't interfear in other people's business.

4. Add *ion* to *confess* to make an abstract noun.

5. Circle the word that adds a final *s* in its plural.

goose   spoon   fish

6. Circle the correct word.

His **rein/rain/reign** ended after his brother defeated him in battle and took the throne.

7. Shorten *has* and *not*.

8. A similar meaning to *aggressive* is

[   ].

calm   gentle   attacking

9. *goal* or *gaol* ?

His brother, the new king, kept him in [   ] for many years.

10. Circle the verb and the adverb that tells when.

When he was finally released, he was an old man.

11. Circle the conjunction.

He was poorly treated while he was in prison.

12. Write with punctuation.

Mount everest is in china and nepal.

MY SCORE

WEEK 19

Using Adjectives to Compare Things

When we compare two people or things, we change the adjective. This is usually done by adding *er*.

*This tree is **tall**, but that tree is **taller**.*

When we compare three or more people or things, we also change the adjective. This is usually done by adding **est**.

*This tree is **tall**, but that tree is **taller**. The tree over there is the **tallest**.*

Although for some words, this does not work; for example, the adjectives in this sentence do not sound right:

*The rose is **beautiful**. The poppy is **beautifuller**. The tulip is **beautifullest**.*

It is not correct to add er or est to these types of adjectives when we are comparing the things they describe.

Instead, we use **more** or **most** before them.

*The rose is **beautiful**. The poppy is **more beautiful**. The tulip is the **most beautiful**.*

Practice Questions

1. Use adjectives to compare the animals.

   The dog is small. The cat is [_____].

   The mouse is the [_____].

2. Which word uses **most** when comparing things?

   expensive   cheap   [_____]

1. Circle the word that uses **most** when comparing more than two things.

   healthy   athletic   fit

2. Use adjectives to compare the family.

   My brother is tall, my mother is [_____]

   and my father is the [_____].

3. Circle the errors. Write them correctly.

   He usualy plays his gitar well.

   [_____] [_____]

4. Add **sub** meaning **under** to **marine** and **divide**.

   [_____] [_____]

5. Which word is first in alphabetical order?

   fluid   flutter   fluster   fluke   flush

6. Tick the meaning of the word **fluke**.

   • a musical instrument [ ]

   • a stroke of good luck [ ]

7. Shorten **would** and **have**.

   [_____]

8. Add **accept** or **except**.

   I would love to [_____] *your invitation.*

9. Circle the two pronouns.

   I received the invitation and sent a reply to him.

10. Circle the noun the pronoun **it** refers to.

    As soon as the invitation arrived, it was answered.

11. Write a question word to start the sentence.

    [_____] *will happen at the party?*

12. Add punctuation.

    I'm so excited [ ]

MY SCORE

Day 2

1. Circle the word that adds **est** when comparing more than two things.

   fantastic   wonderful   great

2. Add **er** or **est** to the adjective **happy**.

   I feel happy in school, I feel [ ] at

   break time, but I feel the [ ] at the end of the day.

3. Rearrange the letters to spell a word that means to **get away**.

   [e] e p a s c e

4. Add **sub** meaning **under** to **heading** and **merge**.

   [ ] [ ]

5. Circle the word that is first in alphabetical order.

   mammoth   malaria   malignant

6. Tick the meaning of the word **solemn**.

   • dangerous and harmful [ ]

   • serious and gloomy [ ]

7. A similar meaning to **starve** is [ ].

   feed   provide   perish

8. Add **accept** or **except**.

   He invited everyone [ ] me.

9. Circle the verb and underline the pronoun.

   We saw Aunt Fiona at the supermarket.

10. The noun the pronoun **it** refers to is [ ].

    The party is a special one and it will be great fun.

11. Write a question word to start this sentence.

    [ ] will win all the prizes?

12. Add speech marks for direct speech.

    Don't worry. Let's go to the cinema, said Mum.

    [ ]

MY SCORE

Day 3

1. Circle the word that uses **most** when comparing more than two things.

   young   careful

2. Add **tiny, tinier** or **tiniest**.

   All those pups are [ ], but that one is

   the [ ].

3. Correct the spelling error.

   I would like to arrang an appointment with you.

   [ ]

4. Add **ation** to **admire** and **prepare** to make abstract nouns.

   [ ] [ ]

5. Write the singular of each word.

   torches boxes glasses potatoes lashes quizzes

   [ ] [ ] [ ]

   [ ] [ ] [ ]

6 Circle the correct word.

   This **pair/pear** is so delicious I could eat another one.

7. Shorten **I** and **will**. [ ]

8. **past** or **passed**?

   We walk [ ] that playground every day.

9. Circle the conjunction.

   We will play on the swings if we have time.

10. Circle the three adjectives.

    The playground is safe and secure for small children.

11. Write a question word to start this sentence.

    [ ] do you know that?

12. Add speech marks.

    I really don't like the climbing frames, I replied.

MY SCORE

Day 4

1. Circle the word that adds **est** when comparing more than two things.

   pretty   famous   charming

2. Add **er** or **more** to the adjective **tall**.

   She was [_____] than most other actresses.

3. Rearrange the letters to spell a word that means something **old and valuable**.

   a [_____] t a n u q i e

4. Add **ation** to **sense** and **perspire**.

   [_____] [_____]

5. Write the singular of each word.

   lunches foxes gases echoes leashes waltzes

   [_____] [_____] [_____]

   [_____] [_____] [_____]

6. Write **pair** or **pear**.

   This [_____] of boots is too small for me.

7. The opposite of **continue** is [_____].

   cease   last   persist

8. **past** or **passed**?

   We always meet on Monday at five [_____] four.

9. Circle the conjunction.

   Unless she misses her bus, Fiona is always early.

10. Circle the two adjectives.

    I enjoy spending time with such a friendly and happy girl.

11. Write a question word to start this sentence.

    [_____] left Italy first?

12. Add punctuation.

    Fiona said that she left Italy when she was two

    MY SCORE

Day 5

1. Circle the word that uses **most** when comparing more than two things.

   fluffy   sweet   obedient

2. **beautiful** or **beautifulest**?

   It was the most [_____] dog.

3. Circle the errors. Write them correctly.

   He is very stronge even thow he is thin.

   [_____] [_____]

4. Add **super** meaning **above** or **over** to **human** and **market**.

   [_____] [_____]

5. Which word is first in alphabetical order?

   homework   homonym   homograph   homesick

6. Tick the meaning of the word **implement**.

   • a mistake   [ ]

   • a tool   [ ]

7. Shorten **he** and **had**. [_____]

8. Add **dessert** or **desert**.

   The lost men searched for water in the

   [_____].

9. Circle the conjunction.

   They staggered through the sand because it was hot.

10. Circle the verb.

    They scooped up cool water with their hands.

11. Write a question word to start this sentence.

    [_____] did you come from?

12. Add punctuation.

    I saw a picture of roald dahl

    MY SCORE

Groups of Things

A noun is a word used to name people, places and things like objects or animals.

Groups of people, places and things often have special words to describe them.

These are called **collective nouns**.

Some other collective nouns include:

people	places	objects	animals
A **class** of children.	A **chain** of islands.	A **clutch** of eggs.	A **colony** of ants.
An **army** of soldiers.	A **range** of mountains.	A **bouquet** of flowers.	A **flock** of sheep.
A **team** of players.	An **alliance** of countries.	A **pair** of shoes.	A **pack** of wolves.

Can you think of any others?

Practice Questions

1. Write the collective noun.

   The stack of papers is sitting on the table.

2. Circle the correct collective noun.

   A choir of singers.

   A choir of soldiers.

1. Write the collective noun.

   Look at the flock of sheep grazing.

2. Circle the correct collective noun.

   A bouquet of flowers or a handful of flowers.

3. Circle the errors. Write them correctly.

   He has a new mobill fone.

4. Add **super** meaning **above** or **over** to **man** and **star**.

5. Which word is last in alphabetical order?

   staple   starch   starve   start   star

6. Tick the meaning of the word **parliament**.

   • a group of people who make the laws ☐

   • a place where men go ☐

7. Write the noun that names a feeling.

   delighted   pie   plate   spoon

8. Add **dessert** or **desert**.

   Would you like some apple pie for ___?

9. Which word uses **more** to compare two things?

   satisfied   hungry

10. Circle the verb and underline the pronouns.

    I ate it with a spoon.

11. Add the missing question word.

    ___ *plate is yours?' asked Mum.*

12. Add speech marks.

    That was the best pie you have ever made! I complimented Mum.

MY SCORE

WEEK 20

Day 2

1. Circle the collective noun.

   The pride of lions stared at the antelope.

2. Is the underlined word a collective noun?

   yes ☐   no ☐

   In the park, there was a swarm of bees.

3. Rearrange the letters to spell a word that means **always on time**.

   p [   ]   t u n c u p a l

4. Add **ation** to **limit** and **plant**.

   [   ]   [   ]

5. Write the plural of **bunch** and **dish**.

   [   ]   [   ]

6. **Sweat** and **perspiration**. Similar or opposite meanings?

   [   ]

7. Circle the correct word.

   *The cowboy rode his horse across the **plain/plane**.*

8. Add **its** or **it's**.

   I enjoy watching a film, especially if [   ] about cowboys.

9. **was** or **were**?

   The cowboy [   ] wearing a hat.

10. Circle the three nouns.

    The cowboy rides away on his horse in the film.

11. Write a question word to start this sentence.

    [   ] *is he waving that flag?*

12. Add speech marks.

    What a hero! I exclaimed.

Day 3

1. Circle the collective noun.

   The band of musicians had a meeting.

2. Circle the correct collective noun.

   a team of horses *or* **a team of foxes**

3. Correct the spelling error.

   After dinner, we watched a televishun show.

   [   ]

4. Add **ation** to **determine** and **populate**.

   [   ]   [   ]

5. Write the plural of **tomato** and **class**.

   [   ]   [   ]

6. **Small** and **mammoth**. Similar or opposite meanings?

   [   ]

7. Circle the correct word.

   *I don't like fancy shirts; **plain/plane** ones are better.*

8. Write **his** or **he's**.

   I can't find my brother. I think [   ] hiding.

9. **did** or **done**?

   I [   ] all the work by myself.

10. Circle the pronoun and underline the conjunction.

    John came back in although he did not speak a word.

11. Write a question word for this question.

    [   ] *were you?' I demanded.*

12. Add speech marks.

    Why didn't you help? I asked.

MY SCORE

MY SCORE

Day 4

1. Circle the collective noun.

   Mum bought a big bunch of grapes in the shop.

2. Is the underlined word a collective noun?

   yes ☐   no ☐

   The battle was won by the better army.

3. Rearrange the letters to spell a word meaning a **part of a whole**.

   [f   ] f a t n i o r c

4. Add **super** meaning **above** or **over** to **natural** and **model**.

   [   ] [   ]

5. Circle the third word in alphabetical order.

   tomato   tomorrow   tolerate   tornado   together

6. Tick the meaning of the word **disability**.

   • a lack of strength making it hard to do things ☐

   • not trying hard enough to do something ☐

7. Write the noun that names a feeling.

   [   ]

   chocolate   bicycle   peace   piece

8. Add **passed** or **past**.

   The ball won't get [   ] *the skilful goalkeeper.*

9. Which word uses **most** to compare a number of things?

   successful   big   [   ]

10. Circle two adverbs.

    Our team battled bravely and won convincingly.

11. Write a question word for this question.

    [   ] *scored the first goal?*

12. Add punctuation.

    what a victory announced the commentator.

MY SCORE

Day 5

1. Circle the collective noun.

   The magician had a pack of cards.

2. Circle the correct collective noun.

   a pack of wolves *or* **a pack of singers**

3. Circle the error. Write it correctly.

   This school chior always sings well.

   [   ]

4. Add **super** meaning **above** or **over** to **power** and **sonic**.

   [   ] [   ]

5. Circle the first word in alphabetical order.

   spell   speed   special   sparkle

6. Tick the meaning of the word **simple**.

   • a one and only ☐

   • easy to understand or do ☐

7. Circle the noun that names a feeling.

   computer   sorrow   actor   magazine

8. Add **passed** or **past**.

   My mum [   ] *me my ticket to the concert.*

9. Which word uses **most** to compare a number of things?

   angry   welcome   [   ]

10. Circle the verb and underline the adjective.

    The chocolates I ate during the concert were delicious.

11. Write a question word for this sentence.

    [   ] *many chocolates are left?*

12. Add punctuation.

    Can I have some he begged

    [   ]

MY SCORE

Root Words

Groups of letters are often added to the beginning and ending of words to change their meaning.

Without these endings, the **base words** still make sense on their own.

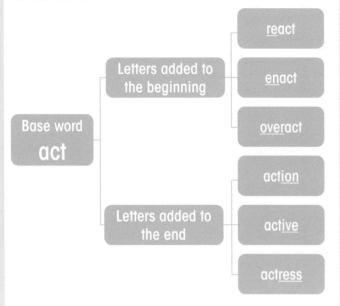

Sometimes, beginnings and endings may be added to words that do not make sense on their own.

| jeal | ous | | sub | tract | | vis | ion | | inter | rupt |

These types of words are called **root words**.

They are words that come from their original language, like French, Greek or Latin.

Root words may or may not make sense once the letters at the beginning or end are removed.

This is also the reason why some groups of letters added to the beginning or end of words do not always have the same meaning.

For example, 'tri' means 'three' in the words 'tricycle' and 'triceratops' but not in 'tribute'.

Practice Questions

1. What is the root word in this word family?

   speaker   spoke   unspoken   speaking

2. Which word can have **re** taken off and still be a base word?

   renovate   rearrange   relative

---

1. What is the root word in this word family?

   likeable   unlikely   dislike   lifelike

2. Which word can have the **sub** taken off and still be a base word?

   submerge   subtract   subject

3. Correct the spelling error.

   I was given a geografy award at our assembly.

4. Add **ous** to **poison** and **danger**.

5. Write the plural of **woman** and **human**.

6. Circle the correct words.

   *I saw a **dear/deer** little **dear/deer** in the forest.*

7. Add a shortened word that makes sense.

   After _____ *finished their training, we'll meet them for a meal.*

8. **Enough** and **adequate**. Similar or opposite meanings?

9. **of** or **off**?

   The two _____ *them got into trouble.*

10. Circle the correct verb.

    *My friends and I (**ate, eats**) some pizza after training.*

11. Circle the collective noun.

    Our team always enjoys eating pizza after we've finished.

12. Punctuate.

    Isn't this the best pizza ever I asked

MY SCORE

Day 2

1. What is the root word in this word family?

greatness   greatly   greatest   greater

2. Which word can have the **ous** taken off and still be a base word?

tremendous   poisonous   jealous

3. Rearrange the letters to spell a word meaning to **lift something up**.

r   r s i a e

4. Add **ous** to **mountain** and **poison** to make nouns.

5. Write the plural of **goose** and **foot**.

6. Circle the correct words.

We **herd/heard** a **herd/heard** of elephants.

7. Add a shortened word that makes sense.

Dad's car won't start, so [   ] have to walk to work.

8. **Parched** and **dry**. Similar or opposite meanings?

9. **cloths** or **clothes**?

His work [   ] weren't suitable.

10. Circle the correct verb.

After walking so far, Dad and Mum (**was, were**) hot and tired.

11. Circle the noun that names a feeling.

Much to Dad's relief, it was just out of petrol.

12. Add capital letters.

mr jones told dad that he must always keep an eye on the fuel gauge.

Day 3

1. Which word does not belong in this word family?

century   centigrade   central

2. Which word can have the **re** taken off and still be a base word?

replay   result   recognise

3. Circle the errors. Write them correctly.

Gray volcanick ash was everywhere.

4. Add **ous** to **humour** and **glamour**.

5. Does **contra** in **contradict** mean **against** or **away**?

6. Circle the last word in alphabetical order.

pouch   powder   poverty   potion

7. Tick the meaning of the word **poverty**.

• a shortage of something needed [ ]

• a horrible place [ ]

8. **Separate** and **apart**. Similar or opposite meanings?

9. Add **raise** or **rise**.

This rain will [   ] the water level of the dam.

10. Circle the noun.

I hope this very welcome rain continues to fall.

11. Add the collective noun. **bunch** or **pack**

We played with a [   ] of cards.

12. Add punctuation.

You're out I'm the winner

MY SCORE

MY SCORE

Day 4

1. What is the root word in this word family?

   actor   action   actress   acting

2. Which word would not be a base word if the **ous** was removed?

   enormous   dangerous   mountainous

3. Rearrange the letters to spell a word that means a **huge piece of land on Earth's surface, like Europe**.

   c   n i t c o n e n t

4. Add **ous** to **vigour** and **odour**.

5. Does **pro** in **progress** and **propel** mean **over** or **forward**?

6. Circle the first word in alphabetical order.

   thunder   timber   thumb   thump

7. Tick the meaning of the word **evident**.

   • a really bad dent in metal ☐

   • very clear and obvious ☐

8. **Astonished** and **surprised**. Similar or opposite meanings?

9. Add **raise** or **rise**.

   If Mum adds this flour, her cake will

   _____.

10. Circle the noun.

    She always bakes the most delicious cakes.

11. Add the collective noun. **bunch** or **bundle**

    Mum bought a _____ of bananas.

12. Add punctuation.

    Banana cakes, my favourites

    MY SCORE

Day 5

1. What is the root word in this word family?

   strongly   stronger   strongest

2. Which word can have the **bi** taken off and still be a base word?

   bicycle   bitter   billion

3. Correct the spelling error.

   An erthquake caused our pipes to burst.

4. Add **ous** to **envy** and **fury**.

5. Circle the word which doesn't have **v** in its plural.

   wharf   half   roof   life

6. Circle the correct words.

   When I go **by/buy/bye** that shop, I'll **by/buy/bye** you a new raincoat.

7. Add a shortened word that makes sense.

   By the look of those dark clouds, I think

   _____ rain.

8. **Modern** and **antique**. Similar or opposite meanings?

9. **break** or **brake**?

   The woman in the car accident was very lucky

   because she did not _____ any bones.

10. Circle the two nouns.

    This rain has been falling for days.

11. Is **concern** a noun that names a feeling?

    yes ☐   no ☐

    The worried farmers show concern for their crops.

12. Add capital letters.

    Since may, more rain has fallen in ireland than in wales.

    MY SCORE

Mine, Yours, Ours

Pronouns are words that are used to replace a noun. Some **pronouns** include:

I   me   we   us   them   they   he   she   him   her

Some pronouns tell who something belongs to.

mine   ours   yours   his   hers   its   theirs

We use these words instead of repeating the noun.

This book is **<u>my book</u>** – It is **<u>mine</u>**.

That dog is **<u>our dog</u>** – It is **<u>ours</u>**.

Those pencils are **<u>Ben's pencils</u>** – They are **his**.

Using pronouns helps you avoid repetition and makes your writing more interesting to read.

Practice Questions

1. Circle all the pronouns that tell who something belongs to.

   I   ours   us   his   theirs   we   they

2. Add the correct pronouns.

   (a) This is Mum's bag. It is [   ].

   (b) This is Dad's hat. It is [   ].

   (c) This is where we all live. This house is

   [   ].

1. Circle the pronoun.

   That dog looks like mine.

2. Which two words are pronouns in this sentence?

   [   ] and [   ]

   They said the poor injured animal was theirs.

3. Correct the spelling error.

   I heard about the storm that distroyed the town.

   [   ]

4. What is the root word in this word family?

   openly   opened   openess   reopen

   [   ]

5. Circle the correct words.

   *They waved to me and said **by/buy/bye** as they walked **by/buy/bye**.*

6. Add a shortened word that makes sense.

   I think [   ] going in their car.

7. **Stationary** and **moving**. Similar or opposite meanings?

   [   ]

8. **break** or **brake**?

   The woman was in the car accident because she did not press the [   ] in time.

9. The word **that** is used for people, things or both?

   [   ]

10. Circle the adjectives.

    The ancient castle has spectacular views over the sea.

11. **Oldest** or **most old**?

    The [   ] wooden drawbridge can still be seen.

12. Add capital letters.

    We were staying in ireland last august and went to visit dublin castle.

MY SCORE

Day 2

1. Circle the pronoun.

   That ice cream is hers.

2. Which two words are pronouns in this sentence?

   [   ] and [   ]

   I like mine with sprinkles on top.

3. Rearrange the letters to spell a word that means **more than one thing**.

   [p   ] r u l a l p

4. Circle the words that are singular and plural.

   trout   scissors   deer   dozen

5. Circle the word which is last in alphabetical order.

   father   fawn   fault   fatigue   fauna

6. Tick the meaning of the word **fatigue**.

   • mental or physical tiredness [ ]

   • foolishness [ ]

7. **Bow** or **bough**? Circle the correct words.

   *Robin Hood used his **bow/bough** and arrow to shoot a target on a **bow/bough** of the tree.*

8. Circle the correct word for comparing two things.

   *Robin Hood was a **better/best** archer than Little John.*

9. Circle the verb group.

   Robin's men had been hiding in the forest.

10. Write the verb and adverb that tells how.

    [   ] [   ]

    His men were secretly hiding from the sheriff's men.

11. Circle the adjective.

    This forest is scary.

12. Add speech marks.

    Where can they be? he asked.

MY SCORE

Day 3

1. Circle the pronoun.

   Is that rubbish yours?

2. Which two words are pronouns in this sentence?

   [   ] and [   ]

   We admitted that the mess was ours.

3. Circle the error. Write the sentence correctly.

   Dad's classick car won an award.

   [   ]

4. What is the root word in this word family?

   approval   disapprove   preapprove

   [   ]

5. Circle the word which is last in alphabetical order.

   mural   mumps   muscle   mumble   munch

6. Tick the meaning of the word **munch**.

   • to eat lunch early [ ]

   • to chew noisily [ ]

7. **Bow** or **bough**? Circle the correct words.

   *I tied a ribbon in a big **bow/bough** on the **bow/bough** of the tree.*

8. Circle the correct word for comparing three things.

   *I chose the **brighter/brightest** ribbon in the shop.*

9. Circle the verb group.

   My friend will find my brightly coloured ribbon.

10. Write the verb and adverb that tells how.

    [   ] [   ]

    My friend looked thoroughly.

11. Circle the adjectives.

    The ribbon is pink with blue spots.

12. Add speech marks.

    Here it is! I've got it! she cried.

MY SCORE

Day 4

1. Circle the pronoun.

   Those sweets are theirs.

2. Which three words are pronouns in this sentence?

   [ ] , [ ] and [ ]

   I was finished, but he was still eating his.

3. Rearrange the letters to spell a word meaning a **person living close by.**

   [n] n g h e b i r o u

4. Circle the words that are singular and plural.

   sheep   salmon   clippers   dozen

5. Circle the correct words.

   I hope your sore **heel/heal** *will* **heel/heal** *quickly.*

6. Shorten **that** and **would**.

   [ ]

7. **Hideous** and **perspiration**. Similar or different meanings?

   [ ]

8. **have** or **of**?

   I could [ ] *caught an earlier bus.*

9. Add the missing word. **who/that/whose**

   That's the old lady [ ] *bird escaped.*

10. Can the word **whose** be used for people, things or both?

    [ ]

11. Circle the correct word for comparing three things.

    I think the **prettier/prettiest** *bird in that tree must be hers.*

12. Add punctuation.

    Thank you, thank you so much! the old lady cried. Then she smiled and gave me a reward.

Day 5

1. Circle the pronoun.

   That car is similar to ours.

2. Which two words are pronouns in this sentence?

   [ ] and [ ]

   She said the car was hers.

3. Correct the spelling error.

   I just can't continue walking any firther.

   [ ]

4. What is the root word in this word family?

   holiday   holiness

   [ ]

5. Circle the correct word.

   Are you **aloud/allowed** *to read* **aloud/allowed**?

6. The shortened word **that's** is made from the word

   that and [ ] or [ ] .

7. **Courteous** and **polite**. Similar or opposite meanings?

   [ ]

8. **have** or **of** ?

   I must [ ] *left my homework on the bus.*

9. Add the missing word. **who/whose/which**

   The bus [ ] *left took my homework.*

10. Can the word **which** be used for people, things or both?

    [ ]

11. **busiest** or **most busy**?

    For me, Saturday is the [ ] *day of the week.*

12. Add capital letters.

    we had to write a report about christopher columbus and his voyage to america.

MY SCORE

MY SCORE

WEEK 23

Words That Show Connections

When writing a sentence, we often use certain words to show how things are connected.

For example, how could you explain this picture to someone who can't see it?

You may have said something like:

A bird is __in__ its nest. The nest is __at__ a park. A butterfly is flying __towards__ the bird.

The words __in__, __at__ and __towards__ show how the things we are talking about are connected.

They tell us the *position* of the bird, the *place* its nest is located and the *direction* the butterfly is going.

There are lots of other words that can be used to show connections between two things in a sentence.

above   around   for   on   to   with   beside   through

Can you think of any others?

Practice Questions

1. Write the missing word for each question. *in at*

    (a) We bought the flowers [ ] the shop.

    (b) The pretty flowers are [ ] the vase.

2. Circle the word that connects the *vase* and the *windowsill*.

    Dad put the vase on the windowsill.

1. Add the word needed to complete the sentence: *to, for, on* or *at*.

    He jumped [ ] *his horse and waved.*

2. Circle the word that connects the horse and the stable.

    The horse in the stable.

3. Circle the errors and write them correctly.

    Put the spagetti in the shopping trolly.

    [ ]   [ ]

4. Add *ful* to *wonder* and *delight*.

    [ ]   [ ]

5. Write the plural of *directory* and *Saturday*.

    [ ]   [ ]

6. Write the next word in alphabetical order.

    uptake or *uptight*?   uprising,   uproar,   upset,

    [ ]

7. Tick the meaning of the word *enthusiastic*.

    • full of positive energy [ ]

    • giving money to a charity [ ]

8. Add *me* or *I*.

    I lost some money while my friend and [ ]

    were at the fair, so she shared hers with [ ].

9. Circle the better conjunction. *because* or *although*.

    We had a good time. We didn't have a lot of money.

10. Circle the verb group.

    My friend has been very generous and kind to me.

11. Which two words are pronouns in this sentence?

    [ ] and [ ]

    The prizes we won were ours.

12. Add a comma.

    Next time I'll carry my money in a wallet. [ ]

    MY SCORE

Day 2

1. Write in the missing word. *for, at, beside*

   The mechanic said he'd go and look

   [ ] the car.

2. Circle the word that connects the **car** and the **garage**.

   The car beside the garage.

3. Rearrange the letters to spell a word meaning **behaving badly**.

   [n] n g h a u t y

4. Add **ful** to **pain** and **help**.

   [ ] [ ]

5. Circle the words where **mis** can be taken off and real base words are left.

   mislead   misfortune   missile   mishap

6. Write the next word in a dictionary.

   tattoo or **tasty**?   tarnish,   tart,   taste,

   [ ]

7. Tick the meaning of the word **annual**.

   • an event to remember [ ]

   • something that happens every year [ ]

8. Add **me** or **I**.

   Our riding school promised to provide Jane and

   [ ] with horses for the show.

9. Circle the better conjunction. **before** or **while**

   We groomed them. We took them to the show.

10. Circle the verb group.

    My horse was frightened by all the noisy people.

11. Which two words are pronouns in this sentence?

    The horse she rode was hers.

    [ ] and [ ]

12. Add a comma.

    Later that afternoon I also won an event.

Day 3

1. Write in the missing word. *for, to, at*

   Most afternoons, I go [ ] the local pool for a swim.

2. Circle the word that connects the **towels** and the **tree**.

   We put our towels under the tree.

3. Correct the spelling error.

   Dad bought a car magazeen in the shop.

   [ ]

4. Add **ly** to **selfish** and **brief**.

   [ ] [ ]

5. Write the plural of **person** and **moose**.

   [ ] [ ]

6. Circle the correct words.

   *I've **seen/scene** this play before but I can't remember what happens in this **seen/scene**.*

7. Shorten **we** and **will**. [ ]

8. **Abbreviate** and **shorten**. Similar or opposite meanings?

   [ ]

9. **led** or **lead**?

   The actor who plays the [ ] *in the play is great.*

10. Underline two verbs and circle the adverbs that tell how.

    He sings beautifully and moves gracefully across the stage.

11. Cross out the word which does not belong.

    As the final curtain fell, everyone stood and cheered up.

12. Add an apostrophe.

    One of the leading actors awards was stolen.

MY SCORE

MY SCORE

Day 4

1. Add the word needed to complete the sentence: **to, with, at** or **for**.

   The boy is sitting [   ] his mum.

2. Circle the word that connects the **concert** and the **school**.

   They are waiting to see the concert at school.

3. Rearrange the letters to spell a word that means **the top of the water**.

   s [   ] c a s e f u r

4. Add **ly** to **brave** and **polite**.

   [   ] [   ]

5. Circle the words where **dis** can be taken off and real base words are left.

   disagree   distance   discipline   disbelieve

6. Circle the correct words.

   After a long drought, the worried **baron/barren** came to see how **baron/barren** his land was looking.

7. Shorten **why** and **is**. [   ]

8. **Dispute** and **agree**. Similar or opposite meanings?

   [   ]

9. **led** or **lead**?

   He [   ] his men to every part of his estate.

10. Underline two verbs and circle the adverbs that tell how.

    The men watched them warily as they moved silently.

11. Cross out the word which does not belong.

    If it doesn't rain soon, any people and animals might suffer.

12. Add an apostrophe.

    The cows body looked thin and bony.

    MY SCORE

Day 5

1. Add the word needed to complete the sentence: **to, with, at** or **for**.

   He was playing [   ] his friend's house.

2. Circle the word that connects the **boardgames** and the **grass**.

   They played boardgames on the grass.

3. Circle the errors and write them correctly.

   This seson the wether is terrible.

   [   ] [   ]

4. Add **ful** to **mouth** and **forget**.

   [   ] [   ]

5. Circle the incorrect plural.

   gentlemans   trousers   reindeer

6. Write the next word in alphabetical order.

   rewind or **reword**?   replay   return   revise

   [   ]

7. Tick the meaning of the word **drought**.

   • a long period of dry weather [   ]

   • a game played with counters [   ]

8. Add **they** or **them**.

   The farmers were concerned about their animals because [   ] didn't have food for [   ].

9. Circle the better conjunction. **Unless** or **While**

   [   ] it rained soon, their crops would die.

10. Circle the verb group.

    They had been looking for clouds in the sky every day.

11. Which two words are pronouns in this sentence?

    They hoped that the rain would come soon and fill the dams that were theirs.

    [   ] and [   ]

12. Add a comma.

    At long last some black clouds appeared and poured with rain.

    MY SCORE

Day 1

1. Circle the error and write it correctly.

   My birthday is in Aurgust.

2. Add **ful** to **harm** and **power**.

3. Circle the two words where **mis** can be taken off and real base words are left.

   mist   misuse   mistrust   missing

4. Write the next word in alphabetical order.

   refuse or **refund**?   reflect,   reform,   refresh,

5. Tick the meaning of the word **relative**.

   • a story that you tell to others ☐

   • a person who is part of your family ☐

6. Add **her** or **she**.

   I like ☐ *because* ☐ *is very kind.*

7. Is the verb in the **past, present** or **future** tense?

   She often helps us with our homework.

8. Circle the verb group.

   She has been doing this for two years.

9. Write the conjunction.

   She might give us cake if we finish our homework.

10. Cross out the word which does not belong.

    She never bakes delicious cakes every weekend.

11. Add the word needed to complete the sentence: **inside, with, at** or **for**.

    A delicious, pink filling was ☐ *the cake.*

12. Add punctuation.

    three cheers for mrs tan! cried the children

    MY SCORE

Day 2

1. Rearrange the letters to spell a word meaning the **day after today**.

   t ☐   *t m r r o w o o*

2. Add **ful** to **beauty** and **duty**.

3. Write the plural of **kitchen** and **lunch**.

4. Circle the correct word.

   *They moved their cattle to **higher/hire** ground after the flood.*

5. Shorten **you** and **will**.

6. **Spacious** and **small**. Similar or opposite in meaning?

7. **her** or **she**?

   Dad needed ☐ *because he knew* ☐ *was good at working with cattle.*

8. Circle a collective noun to complete each phrase.

   • a **herd/mob** of cattle ☐

   • a **swarm/flock** of sheep ☐

9. Circle the command.

   Close that gate. The gate is open. Is the gate open?

10. Which verb? **did** or **done**

    The truck driver ☐ *a great job loading the cattle.*

11. Circle the past tense verbs.

    *The truck driver **drives/drove** off and **waves/waved** to me.*

12. Add three commas.

    In the morning I'll have to get up early have breakfast saddle my horse and get some more cattle.

    MY SCORE

Day 3

1. Correct the spelling error.

   The freindship we share is very important to me.

2. Add **ful** to **pity** and **plenty**.

3. Write the singular of **potatoes** and **tomatoes**.

4. Circle the correct word.

   *I had to **higher/hire** a car when my car broke down.*

5. Shorten **she** and **has**.

6. **Thorough** and **careful**. Similar or opposite meanings?

7. **her** or **she**?

   I'm not sure if that's [ ] *driving a blue car, doesn't* [ ] *usually drive a red one?*

8. Add a collective noun. **fleet/flock**

   There are a [ ] *of vehicles in the car park.*

9. Circle the statement.

   Will the car start? It won't start. Take my car.

10. Which verb? **had** or **has**.

    My car won't start because it [ ] *a flat battery.*

11. Circle the present tense verbs.

    *I **am/was** lucky that Mum **lets/let** me take her car.*

12. Add two commas.

    On these occasions my wonderful mum picks up her bag walks to the bus stop and catches a bus to work.

    MY SCORE

Day 4

1. Rearrange the letters to spell a word meaning a **place for the sick**.

   [h]   h p o s i a l t

2. Add **ly** to **special** and **personal**.

3. Change the vowels to make the words plural.

   goose foot

4. Is the next alphabetical order word **porthole** or **portraif**?

   porter   portfolio   portion

5. Tick the meaning of the word **hideous**.

   • very ugly   [ ]

   • hidden   [ ]

6. Add **did** or **done**.

   Who [ ] *that?*

7. Is the verb in the **past, present** or **future** tense?

   My parents bought me a new bike.

8. Circle the verb group.

   I have been riding my new bike everywhere.

9. Circle a conjunction to join these two sentences. **after** or **while**

   I was sleeping. Someone took my bike.

10. Cross out the word which does not belong.

    The thieves didn't not keep my bike for very long.

11. Add the word needed to complete the sentence: **inside, under, at** or **for**.

    A man found my bike [ ] *a tree outside the school.*

12. Add punctuation.

    can I get a new bike? I begged

    MY SCORE

1. Circle the errors and write them correctly.

   Farming baren land is tuff.

   [ ] [ ]

2. Add *ly* to **final** and **natural**.

   [ ] [ ]

3. Circle the singular words.
   Hint: Many nouns ending in `*is*' change to `*es*' when plural.

   oasis/oases   emphasis/emphases

4. Is the next alphabetical order word **music** or **muscle**?

   munch, mural, murder, [ ],

5. Tick the meaning of the word **oasis**.

   • a meeting place [ ]

   • a place in the desert with water [ ]

6. Add **did** or **done**.

   I don't know who [ ] *it.*

7. Is the verb in the **past, present** or **future** tense?

   My dad rode on a camel with me.

   [ ]

8. Circle the verb group.

   The camel was walking awkwardly through the hot sand.

9. Circle a conjunction to join these two sentences.
   although or **after**

   It was hot. The camels didn't need water.

10. Cross out the word which does not belong.

    The camel has walked through the sand with long, slow steps.

11. Add the word needed to complete the sentence: *in, under* or *along*.

    We went for a camel ride [ ] *the beach at sunset.*

12. Add the missing punctuation.

    'That was great When can we do it again ' I asked.

    MY SCORE [ ]

---

1. Rearrange the letters to spell a word that means an *Irish game played with a small ball*.

   [h] l u r g i n h

2. Does the **pre** in **precook** and **prepay** mean before or after?

   [ ]

3. Write the plural of **axis**.

   [ ]

4. Which word can have the **pre** taken off and still be a base word?

   prepare   preplay   precise

   [ ]

5. Circle the correct word.

   *My friend **bought/brought** a new computer.*

6. Cross out the word that does not belong.

   He already has a computer but he's is not going to use it.

7. Circle the collective noun.

   This suite of furniture is so comfortable.

8. Write the pronoun that shows the owner.

   The computer is his. [ ]

9. Circle the conjunction.

   My mum said that I could get a new computer if I do extra chores.

10. Circle a conjunction to join these two sentences.
    although because

    I will work hard. I would really like a new computer.

11. Add the word needed to complete the sentence: *to, for, on* or *at*.

    We will be looking for a new computer [ ] *Wednesday.*

12. Add an apostrophe.

    My new computer will be better than my mums.

    MY SCORE [ ]

WEEK 25

Words for Males and Females

A noun is a word used to name people, places and things like objects or animals.

Some nouns name male or female people and animals. These are called **gender nouns**.

The nouns for males are called **masculine nouns** and those for females are called **feminine nouns**.

Some masculine and feminine nouns include:

	People	**Animals**
Masculine	boy	rooster
	man	bull
	father	ram
	uncle	drake
Feminine	girl	hen
	woman	cow
	mother	ewe
	aunt	duck

Not all nouns have a gender. Many nouns like person, parents and children have no gender at all.

Practice Questions

1. Circle the feminine noun.

   king   husband   actress

2. Circle the masculine noun.

   lady   sir   niece

1. Masculine nouns or feminine nouns?

   [   ]

   niece   hostess   goose

2. Write the masculine noun of *wife*.

   [   ]

3. Correct the spelling error.

   I observed the submarine submerg and disappear.

   [   ]

4. Add *ly* to *wonderful* and *careful*.

   [   ]   [   ]

5. *Mustn't* is shortened from

   [   ] and [   ].

6. A similar meaning to *proposal*.

   plan   protest   situation

   [   ]

7. Circle the correct words.

   *A brave **night/knight** rode his horse all **night/knight**.*

8. *among* or *between*?
   Hint: between = two items,
   among = three or more items.

   The enemy hid [   ] *all the trees.*

9. Circle the nouns.

   The lone knight rode through the forest to the castle.

10. Circle the adjectives.

    He crossed a steep, rugged mountain.

11. Circle the correct adjective.

    *This mountain was **steeper/more steep** than any other in the kingdom.*

12. Is the punctuation correct? [   ]

    Well done sir William, I knew you wouldn't fail me, said the king.

    MY SCORE

Day 2

1. Circle the two feminine nouns. *drake/duckling/ duck goose/gander/gosling*

2. Write the feminine noun of *wizard*.

3. Rearrange the letters to spell a word that means *not very deep*.

   s [ ] l o w l a h s

4. Add *ly* to *actual* and *artificial*.

5. *How's* is shortened from *how* and [ ] or *how* and [ ] .

6. Circle the opposite of *ruin*.

   wreck   repair   spoil

7. Circle the correct word.

   It took them ten days to reach the mountain peek/peak.

8. *among* or *between*?

   Share the food [ ] *the five climbers.*

9. Circle the nouns.

   It had been a long hard journey, but they finally reached the summit of the mountain.

10. Circle the adjective.

    They enjoyed the stunning view.

11. Circle the correct adjective.

    It was the quietest/most quiet place they'd ever been.

12. Is the punctuation correct?

    Look at that! How beautiful! she gasped.

Day 3

1. Masculine nouns or feminine nouns?

   bride   widow   mare

2. Write the masculine noun of *queen*.

3. Circle the error and write it correctly.

   A shuttel landed on the moon.

4. Add *bi* to *cycle*. [ ]

5. Are these words in alphabetical order?

   heal   hear   heart   heat

6. Tick the meaning of the word *bilateral*.

   • affecting both sides [ ]

   • on the side [ ]

7. Add *good* or *well*.
   Hint: good = adjective,
   well = adverb.

   You played really [ ] *on Saturday.*

8. Circle the noun that names a feeling.

   The enthusiasm of the crowd made his tennis match more exciting for me.

9. Circle the proper nouns.

   Keep practising and perhaps one day you'll be as good as Andy Murray and win Wimbledon.

10. The pronoun *it* refers to [ ] .

    His ball slammed into the net then bounced over it.

11. Circle three pronouns.

    I think the tennis racket you have is mine.

12. Add speech marks.

    Where can they be? he asked.

MY SCORE

MY SCORE

Day 4

1. Circle the two masculine nouns.

   foal/mare/stallion hen/rooster/chicken

2. Write the feminine noun of **king**.

3. Rearrange the letters to spell a word meaning to **keep going**.

   c   c n o t i e u n

4. Circle the word where **bi** means **two**.

   bishop   binoculars   birthday

5. Are these words in alphabetical order?

   funny   furnish   further   furious

6. Tick the meaning of the word **courteous**.

   • attending court ☐

   • well-mannered and polite ☐

7. Add **good** or **well**.

   He was not feeling _____, so he stayed in bed.

8. Circle the noun that **can't be touched** (abstract noun).

   His long illness has been difficult for his family.

9. Circle the nouns.

   The man gave the nurses a card to thank them for looking after him so well.

10. The pronoun **he** refers to _____.

    The doctor told his patient he could go home.

11. Circle the pronoun.

    He couldn't wait to get up and go home.

12. Add speech marks.

    He said, Where are my things?

MY SCORE

Day 5

1. Masculine nouns or feminine nouns?

   bridegroom   nephew   stallion

2. Write the masculine noun of **actress**.

3. Correct the spelling error.

   The kurtain in the window is dusty.

4. Add **ly** to **noisy** and **thirsty**.

5. **You'll** is the shortened word for **you** and

   _____.

6. Circle a similar meaning to **seize**.

   drop   size   grab

7. Circle the correct word.

   I won't wake the baby, I'll just have a quick **peak/peek**.

8. **Really** or **real**?

   The baby is _____ having a good sleep.

9. Circle two nouns (one is an abstract noun).

   That's an unusual name for a boy.

10. Circle the adjective.

    He is such a good baby that I wish he was mine.

11. Add **his** or **theirs**.

    James thinks these toys are _____, but the other babies all think they are _____.

12. Add punctuation.

    'No James You must learn to share' she told him.

MY SCORE

Good and Bad

To compare two or more people or things, we often add **er** or **est** to the end of the adjective.

This light is **bright.**   *This light is* **brighter.**   *This light is the* **brightest.**

However, this does not always work for some words and so we must add another word before the adjective like **more/most** or **less/least.**

That entree was **delicious.** *Dinner was* **more delicious,** *but desert was the* **most delicious.**

Some words do not follow this rule either. Instead, we must change the whole word.

The words **good** and **bad** are two examples of this.

Tom is **good** *at football. Tim is* **better** *at football. Tam is the* **best** *at football.*

I am a bad swimmer. My brother is a **worse** *swimmer. My mum is the* **worst** *swimmer.*

Practice Questions

1. Which word could replace the underlined words?

   I heard the <u>most bad</u> *news today.*

2. Which word could replace the underlined words?

   I felt <u>more good</u> *after my mum gave me a hug.*

1. Which word can be used to compare two things?

   gooder   more good   better

2. Add the correct forms of the adjective.

   I am good at football, my brother is

   _____ *, but my sister is the* _____ .

3. Circle the error and write correctly.

   We were always amung friends.

4. Add **ally** to **magic** and **normal**.

5. **What'll** is shortened from **what** and

   _____ .

6. Circle a similar meaning to **furious**.

   angry   calm   furry

7. Circle the correct word.

   Hasn't your baby **groan/grown?**

8. **really** or **real**?

   That toy cat looks almost _____

9. Add **a** or **an**.

   Would she like _____ *toy giraffe or* _____ *elephant?*

10. Add **me** or **I**.

    Please give her to _____ *so* _____ *can have a cuddle.*

11. Circle the conjunction.

    I know that is yours but I would really like to borrow it.

12. Is the punctuation correct? _____

    Of course you can have a cuddle, his mother replied.

MY SCORE

Day 2

1. Which word can be used to compare three things?

   goodest   most good   best

2. Add the correct forms of the adjective.

   I think broccoli is bad, beans are

   but sprouts are the

3. Rearrange the letters to spell a word meaning **something you hear**.

   n   n s i o e

4. Add **ally** to **tragic** and **frantic**.

5. Are these words in alphabetical order?

   flower   flutter   flush   flute

6. Tick the meaning of the word **frantic**.
   - acting like a fan of a team or person
   - wild with worry or excitement

7. Add **good** or **well**.

   They were a very   team.

8. Add **their** or **there**.

   When we got   , we noticed that

                          door was wide open.

9. Circle the verb group.

   The English team was defeated by the Italian team at Wembley Stadium last Saturday.

10. Add a question word.

                          is the captain of the Irish team?

11. Write the conjunction.

    I love watching football if it's not raining.

12. Add capital letters.

    the german team defeated the
    spanish team.   MY SCORE

Day 3

1. Which word can be used to compare two things?

   worser   more bad   worse

2. Add the correct forms of the adjective.

   Mittens is good at catching mice. Fluffy is

                          at catching mice.

   Snowball is the

3. Circle the error and write it correctly.

   How strange and wierd is that?

4. Add **ly** to **horrible** and **terrible**.

5. Are these words in alphabetical order?

   bitter   biscuit   bird   birth

6. Tick the meaning of the word **flute**.
   - a musical instrument
   - a type of vehicle

7. Add **good** or **well**.

   I hope I am feeling   enough
   to go to school tomorrow.

8. Add **they're** or **there**.

   I don't know why   not

   going   on holiday this year.

9. Circle the adjectives.

   The song has special, happy memories for me.

10. Add a question word.

                          do you prefer that the most?

11. Circle the conjunction.

    I enjoy that band when they are playing dance music.

12. Add speech marks.

    Can you play quietly? he asked.   MY SCORE

Day 4

1. Which word can be used to compare three things?

   worstest   most bad   worst

2. Add the correct forms of the adjective.

   I felt bad on Monday. On Tuesday I felt

   [   ]. Today I feel the [   ].

3. Rearrange the letters to spell a word that means the **biggest amount possible**.

   [m   ]   m u x i m a m

4. Add **ly** to **gentle** and **possible**.

   [   ]   [   ]

5. **What's** is shortened from **what** and **is** or **what** and

   [   ].

6. Circle the opposite of **awkward**.

   clumsy   careful   slow

7. Circle the correct word.

   The **whether/weather** is so bad, I don't know **whether/weather** we should go.

   [   ]

8. **off** or **of**?

   It was so cold I didn't take [   ] my coat.

9. Circle the adjectives.

   Paul's hair is dry, but Tim's feet are wet.

10. Add the missing word. **who/that/whose**

    That's the boy [   ] coat got wet.

11. Circle the conjunction.

    I would have lent him mine if he had asked.

12. Is the punctuation correct? [   ]

    Next time, I'm sure he'll take a raincoat.

Day 5

1. Change these adjectives to the correct form used to compare things.

   good [   ] [   ]

   bad   [   ] [   ]

2. Add the correct forms of the adjective.

   I am good at making pies, Mum is [   ]

   but Granny is the [   ].

3. Circle the errors and write them correctly.

   I'm forteen and Mum's fourty.

   [   ]   [   ]

4. Add **ly** to **easy** and **happy**.

   [   ]   [   ]

5. Shorten **you** and **have**. [   ]

6. Circle a similar meaning to **remarkable**.

   incredible   ordinary   usual

7. Circle the correct word.

   The sailor tied his boat to the **key/quay**, unloaded his bike, turned the **key/quay** and rode off into town.

8. **off** or **of**?

   His bag fell [   ] his bike.

9. Add **a** or **an**.

   He saw [   ] kind lady wave to him from [   ] old shed.

10. Add **who/that/whose**.

    He waved back and hopped on the bike [   ] he always kept on his boat.

11. Write the conjunction. [   ]

    The kind lady rushed over and gave the man the bag he had dropped.

12. Add speech marks to show direct speech.

    Thank you. I am pleased you picked it up before a car ran over it, said the man.

MY SCORE

Tricky Plurals

Showing that we have more than one of something is often as easy as adding an s or es to the end of the noun.

However, sometimes it can be a little trickier.

Some nouns are formed from two words. These are called compound words.

tooth + brush = toothbrush
birth + day = birthday
eye + lash = eyelash

When compound words are joined together to make one word, they follow the same plural rules as other nouns.

toothbrush**es**   birthday**s**   eyelash**es**

However, some compound words stay as two or more separate words that are joined using a small mark called a hyphen.

mother - in - law

great - grandfather

runner - up

When this happens, we must make the most important noun plural.

mothers-in-law

great-**grandfathers**

runners–up

Practice Questions

1. Circle the correct plural.

   greats-grandmother

   sisters-in-law

   merries-go-round

2. Write the plural of **gentleman** and **toothbrush**.

1. Write the plural of **father-in-law**.

2. Circle two incorrect plurals.

   bucketsful   armfuls   handfuls   boxesful

3. Circle the spelling error and rewrite it correctly.

   They found a toomb in the desert.

4. Add **ible** to **collect** and **digest**.

5. Circle the last word in alphabetical order.

   answer   antique   anteater

6. Tick the meaning of the word **asteroid**.

   • something that comes from space ☐

   • a star-shaped punctuation mark ☐

7. Write the correct word for comparing two things.

   gooder   better   more good

8. Add **it's** or **its**.

   The space shuttle separated from ☐ *rocket.*

9. Circle the conjunction.

   The shuttle was finally launched after some technical difficulties had been fixed.

10. Circle the verb group.

    They had been working on this shuttle for months.

11. Is the verb in the **past, present** or **future** tense?

    The information will be examined with great interest by scientists from around the world.

12. Add a comma.

    After two days on the space station they'll return to Earth.

MY SCORE

Day 2

1. Write the plural of **cupful**.

2. Circle the correct plural.

   maids-of-honour   maid-of-honours

3. Rearrange the letters to spell a word that means **not behaving in the right way.**

   m [   ] h a b e m v i s e

4. Which does **astro** in **astronaut** and **astronomy** mean?

   danger   rocket   star

5. Circle the last word in alphabetical order.

   cactus   cabbage   cabin

6. Tick the meaning of the word **sketch**.

   • a quick, rough drawing ☐

   • something that has been stretched ☐

7. Write the correct one for comparing three things.

   the goodest   the most good   the best

8. Add **it's** or **its**.

   I think [   ] hard to sketch people.

9. Circle the conjunction.

   Although she is an excellent artist, her exhibition was not very popular.

10. Circle the verb group.

    She has been painting for over twenty years.

11. Is the verb in the **past, present** or **future** tense?

    I hope her next exhibition will be more successful.

12. Add speech marks.

    When will it be held? I asked.

MY SCORE

Day 3

1. Write the plural of **runner-up**.

2. Circle two incorrect plurals.

   catsfish   ladiesbird   cabbages

3. Correct the spelling error.

   A frase is a group of words in a sentence.

4. Add **able** to **avoid** and **laugh**.

5. Shorten **are** and **not**. [   ]

6. Write an opposite of **assemble** by adding **dis**.

7. Circle the correct word.

   *At **our/hour** school we have one **our/hour** for lunch.*

8. **seen** or **saw**?

   I [   ] you drop that banana skin.

9. Add the words needed to complete the sentence: **to, on, at** or **in**.

   Get that banana skin you dropped [   ] the floor and put it [   ] the bin.

10. Write the adverb.

    It is important to cross the road carefully.

11. Add an apostrophe.

    That schools bell is loud and annoying.

12. Add a comma.

    While you were cleaning up we played a quick game.

MY SCORE

Day 4

1. Write the plural of **spoonful**.

2. Circle the correct plural.

   sisters-in-law   sister-in-laws

3. Rearrange the letters to spell a word meaning **a family member.**

   m   m t o r e h

4. Add **able** to **read** and **enjoy**.

5. Shorten **can** and **not**.

6. Write the opposite of **improbable** by removing two letters.

7. Circle the correct word.

   Whose/Who's coming to the football match?

8. **seen** or **saw**?

   I've   these two teams play before.

9. Add the words needed to complete the sentence: **over, at** or **in**.

   He took a shot   goal, but

   the ball went   the net.

10. Write the adverb.

    He played skilfully during the training session.

11. Add an apostrophe.

    Our captains parents always come to our games.

12. Add punctuation.

    'Go Eagles Get that ball Run, run ' she yelled.

MY SCORE

Day 5

1. Write the plural of **merry-go-round**.

2. Circle two incorrect plurals.

   bathrooms   homeswork   cowsboy

3. Circle the spelling error and rewrite it correctly.

   Our gest is here on holiday.

4. Add **able** to **excite** and **admire**.

5. Circle the word that is last in alphabetical order.

   butcher   button   busy

6. Tick the meaning of the word **plough**.

   • a tool for digging up soil ☐

   • a type of farm ☐

7. Add the correct form of the adjective.

   I am bad at singing, but my mum is [   ].

8. Add **bad** or **badly**.

   Although I have a [   ]

   voice, I [   ] want to be in the school choir.

9. Circle the conjunction.

   My sister has joined a new band and she is singing regularly with them.

10. Circle the verb group.

    I wish I was able to sing in public.

11. Is the verb in the **past, present** or **future** tense?

    Our dog barks if I sing in the house.

12. Add speech marks.

    My mean dad asked, Can you whistle, Ryan? Because you certainly can't sing.

MY SCORE

What is a Simile?

*Emma is as busy **as** a bee.*   *John slept **like** a log.*

Have you ever heard people use sayings like these?

These are a special type of phrase called a **simile**.

A **simile** compares one thing with another and usually uses the words *as* or *like*.

The words used in a simile do not mean what they actually say.

Instead, they are used to create a picture in the reader's mind.

For example, by comparing Emma with a bee, you might imagine her buzzing around quickly like a bee looking for pollen.

Practice Questions

1. Complete the simile.

   as [   ] as honey

2. Which word completes the simile?

   laughs   cries

   My sister [   ] like a hyena.

1. Complete the simile.

   as [   ] as ice

2. Which word completes the simile? *roll* or *sleep*

   [   ] like a log

3. Circle the spelling error and rewrite it correctly.

   We'll go by bus insted of walking.

   [   ]

4. Add *able* to *believe* and *advise*.

   [   ]   [   ]

5. Circle the correct plural.

   sons-in-law   son-in-laws

6. Circle the word that is last in alphabetical order.

   diary   dial   dice   diet

7. Tick the meaning of the word *diary*.

   • a place for cattle   [   ]

   • a written record of events   [   ]

8. Add *bad* or *badly*.

   Your story is [   ] *written and your*

   [   ] *spelling makes it harder to read.*

9. Write the adverb.

   I carefully learnt my spelling last night.

   [   ]

10. Circle the conjunction.

    I practise my spelling on the school bus while my friends talk.

11. Which word needs an apostrophe?

    My friend left her book on another childs desk.

12. Add speech marks.

    Where did I leave my spelling folder? I think it's on the bus! I cried.

MY SCORE

Day 2

1. Complete the simile.

   as [_____] as a pancake

2. Which word completes the simile? **whales** or **peas**

   like [_____] in a pod

3. Rearrange the letters to spell a word meaning to **get ready**.

   [p _____] p e p r e r a

4. Write the opposite of **necessary** by adding two letters.

   [_____]

5. Circle the word which does not add a final **s** in its plural.

   bagful   solution   sister-in-law   bucketful

6. Shorten **why** and **would**. [_____]

7. Circle the correct word.

   If you put your name on your clothes, we'll know **who's/whose** they are.

8. **tried** or **tired**?

   The player [_____] desperately to score a goal.

9. Add the verb **tries** or **try** to match the pronouns.

   We [_____] hard to win, but he [_____] even harder.

10. Circle the verb group.

    He has been an excellent player for our team.

11 Circle the conjunction.

   If you get the ball to Paul, he'll score a goal.

12. Add punctuation.

    great goal, paul! I shouted.

MY SCORE

Day 3

1. Complete the simile.

   as [_____] as a bee

2. Which word completes the simile? **shine** or **swim**

   [_____] like a fish

3. Correct the spelling error.

   I know the anser to that question.

   [_____]

4. The words **notice** and **trace** keep e when adding able. Add **able** to both words.

   [_____] [_____]

5. Circle the correct plural.

   mothers-in-law   mother-in-laws

6. Shorten **how** and **had**. [_____]

7. Circle the correct word.

   The dog always goes into the garden to **berry/bury** his bones.

8. **tried** or **tired**?

   He [_____] to find it, but he was too

   [_____] to keep on digging.

9. Add the verb **go** or **goes** to match the pronouns.

   He [_____] to that school but I [_____] to this one.

10. Circle the verb group.

    I hope he will keep digging tomorrow.

11. Circle the conjunction.

    When my dog finds his bone, he will be happy.

12. Add punctuation.

    I yelled, I think I've found something here, my spade has just hit something hard.

MY SCORE

Day 4

1. Complete the simile.

   as [_____] as a bat

2. Which word completes the simile? **fight** or **love**

   [_____] like cats and dogs

3. Rearrange the letters to spell a word that means **vacation**.

   [h _____] y a h l o i d

4. Write the opposite of **truthful** by adding two letters.

   [_____]

5. Circle the word that adds a final **s** in its plural.

   goose   spoonful   father-in-law   maid-of-honour

6. Circle the last word in alphabetical order.

   even   erupt   escort   establish

7. Tick the meaning of the word **buoyancy**.

   • the ability of something to float in water ☐

   • how bouncy a surface is ☐

8. Is **good** an adjective or an adverb?

   It was a **good** flight and the crew looked after us well.

9. Circle the adverb.

   The flight to Singapore departed punctually at seven a.m.

10. Circle the conjunction.

    Before we touched down, Dad was asked to complete a landing card for customs.

11. Which word needs an apostrophe?

    After the long trip, the ladys legs ached.

    [_____]

12. Add speech marks.

    That took ages! I complained.

MY SCORE

Day 5

1. Complete the simile.

   as [_____] as a gold

2. Which word completes the simile? **fast** or **slow**

   [_____] like lightning

3. Circle the spelling error and rewrite it correctly.

   Did you recieve the letter I sent last Wednesday?

   [_____]

4. The words **love** and **drive** keep e when adding able. Add **able** to both words.

   [_____] [_____]

5. Write the singular of **sisters-in-law.**

   [_____]

6. Circle the last word in alphabetical order.

   fire   finch   final   film   fine

7. Tick the meaning of the word **gnat**.

   • a chat ☐

   • an insect ☐

8. Is **fast** an adjective or an adverb?

   We caught a **fast** train from Cork to Dublin.

9. Circle the adverbs.

   We travelled comfortably although it was raining wildly.

10. Circle the conjunction.

    When we arrived at the station, we caught a bus.

11. Which word needs an apostrophe?

    The rain was making the tourists map wet and soggy.

    [_____]

12. Add speech marks.

    Where am I? Is this the main road? he asked

MY SCORE

Who is Talking?

Speech marks are used to show the *exact* words that are spoken by a person.

This is called **direct speech**.

Sometimes, a spoken sentence is interrupted to show who is speaking.

'I think', said Zoe slowly, 'that we're going to buy a present for Granny'.

When this happens, we must remember three rules:

- Only the exact words said by the speaker are enclosed in speech marks.
- Punctuation (except for question marks and exclamation marks) do not go inside the speech marks.
- The other words, that are not part of the direct speech, do not go inside the speech marks.

Practice Questions

1. Add speech marks.

    The computer is broken, said Mum, but I don't know how to fix it.

2. Add speech marks.

    Stop playing that loud music, shouted our neighbour, or I will tell your dad!

---

1. Add speech marks.

    I'll take more care next time we sail, I promised them, so hopefully we won't be disqualified.

2. Are the speech marks used correctly?

    yes ☐   no ☐

    'OK, captain', said the team sadly, 'better luck next time!'

3. Correct the spelling error.

    I know the truth so don't try to deceeve me.

4. Add **en** to **gold** and **silk** to make adjectives.

5. Complete the simile.

    as [ ] *as a giraffe*

6. **When's** is shortened from **when** and

    [ ] or [ ] .

7. Circle the correct word.

    Our yacht didn't sail around the last **boy/buoy**, *so we were disqualified from the race.*

8. A similar meaning to **transmit** is [ ].

    broadcast   cross   collect

9. **have** or **of** ?

    I must [ ] *been sailing too fast.*

10. Add **who/that/whose.**

    The yacht [ ] *was disqualified is ours.*

11. Add the correct forms of the adjective.

    He is busy, she is [ ], *but I am the* [ ].

12. Circle the feminine noun.

    The servants raced around after the queen.

    MY SCORE

Day 2

1. Add speech marks.

   Well, said my friend as we walked out of the theatre, that play was very funny!

2. Are the speech marks used correctly?

   yes ☐   no ☐

   'I think, I replied,' 'that it was a bit boring'.

3. Rearrange the letters to spell a word that means **damp**.

   [m   ]   s t i o m

4. Add **en** to **sharp** and **length** to make verbs.

   [   ]   [   ]

5. Which word completes the simile? **smokes** or **glows**

   [   ]   *like a chimney*

6. **It's** is shortened form of **it** and

   [   ] or [   ] .

7. Circle the correct word.

   *Please **accept/except** my apologies, but I won't be able to attend your party.*

8. A similar meaning to **supreme** is [   ] .

   supper   greatest   worthwhile

9. **have** or **of**?

   I should [   ] *let you know earlier.*

10. Add **who/that/whose**.

    You're the person [   ] *party I want to attend.*

11. Add the correct forms of the adjective.

    I think running is easy, jogging is [   ] *,*

    but walking is the [   ] *.*

12. Circle the masculine noun.

    The lady told the boy to get his coat.

    MY SCORE

Day 3

1. Add speech marks.

   They're beautiful, I exclaimed, so I bet they're expensive!

2. Are the speech marks used correctly?

   yes ☐   no ☐

   'Why, yes', began the salesman, 'they are very pricey'.

3. Circle the spelling error and rewrite it correctly.

   Draw two straite lines.

   [   ]

4. Add **en** to **white** and **wide** to make verbs.

   [   ]   [   ]

5. Write the plural of the compound noun.

   passer-by [   ]

6. Which word comes before **found** in a dictionary?

   fowl   forward   four   [   ]

7. Tick the meaning of the word **analyst**.

   • a person who knows in detail how something works ☐

   • a person who tries to understand something ☐

8. Add **a** or **an**.

   The gardener used [   ] *axe and*

   [   ] *saw to remove the tree.*

9. Circle the proper nouns.

   The famous Botanical Gardens in Singapore are very beautiful.

10. Circle the adjectives.

    Although the plants are rare and unique, they are amazing.

11. Write the verb. [   ]

    Many tourists visit these gardens every year.

12. Circle the nouns.

    Flowers can be seen everywhere in these gardens.

    MY SCORE

Day 4

1. Add speech marks.

   Maybe one day, he said thoughtfully, we could visit Egypt again.

2. Are the speech marks used correctly?

   yes ☐   no ☐

   'Yes', replied Mum, that would be lovely.

3. Rearrange the letters to spell a word meaning **not old**.

   [y _____]   y n u o g

4. Add **en** to **loose** and **ripe** to make verbs.

   [_____]   [_____]

5. Circle the incorrect plural.

   rainbows   toothbrushes   feetballs

6. Which word comes before **insult** in a dictionary?

   intend interact instruct   [_____]

7. Tick the meaning of the word **pyramid**.

   • a structure built in ancient Egypt ☐

   • a triangle ☐

8. Add **a** or **an**.

   They found [_____] *mummy in* [_____] *ancient tomb.*

9. Circle the nouns.

   The scientists were very excited by this amazing tomb.

10. Circle the adjectives.

    Did you know that rare, ancient treasures are still being found?

11. Write the verb. [_____]

    This mummy is now famous.

12. Circle the nouns.

    People everywhere are fascinated by these ancient artefacts

    MY SCORE

Day 5

1. Add speech marks.

   My favourite books, he said smiling, are the Harry Potter series.

2. Are the speech marks used correctly?

   yes ☐   no ☐

   'Mine, I replied after thinking carefully, would be anything about dragons'.

3. Correct the spelling error.

   I would prefer to just have an ordinery looking dog.

   [_____]

4. Add **en** to **tight** and **sweet** to make verbs.

   [_____]   [_____]

5. Complete the simile.

   as [_____] as a daisy

6. Shorten **she** and **will**. [_____]

7. Circle the correct word.

   *I will **choose/chews** a new book from the library.*

8. A similar meaning to **secure** is

   quick   safe   dangerous

   [_____].

9. **go** or **goes**?

   That book [_____] *on this shelf and these* [_____] *there.*

10. Add **who/that/whose**.

    I have a new book [_____] *you might like to read.*

11. Add the correct forms of the adjective.

    I think information books are good, novels are [_____], *but comics are the* [_____].

12. Circle the feminine noun.

    This lady is great writer and I've read all her books!

    MY SCORE

Bossy Verbs

A verb is a word which shows actions, or states of being or having.

Every sentence must have a verb.

Some verbs are used to order, command or give instructions. They are called **command verbs**.

'**_Tie_** your shoelaces', said Mum.

'**_Put_** your finished work on that pile!' said Mr Smith.

Command verbs are used in command sentences and exclamation sentences.

There are many different command verbs:

bring stop take cut go fold place hold try turn

These verbs are not always used as command verbs.

Remember: to be a command verb, the verb must be telling someone to do something.

Practice Questions

1. Circle the command verbs.

   After school, finish your homework and do your chores.

2. Is this sentence a command or a statement?

   When you have finished, you can watch television.

MY SCORE

1. Circle the command verb.

   Write your name at the top of your work.

2. Tick.

   statement ☐   question ☐   command ☐

   Bring me your completed work.

3. Correct the spelling error.

   Are you sertain you're well enough to continue playing?

4. Add **_acy_** to **_private_** to make a noun.

5. Which word completes the simile? **_sing_** or **_fly_**

   like an angel

6. Shorten **_who_** and **_will_**.

7. Circle the correct word.

   Our puppy **choose/chews** everything we leave on the floor.

8. An opposite of **_constructive_** is

   building   worthwhile   destructive

9. **_am_** or **_are_**?

   _I ___ cross, but I guess all puppies ___ like that._

10. Add the correct form of the adjective.

    _The puppy has been bad, but he was ___ when we first got him._

11. The pronoun **_theirs_** refers to ___.

    Ask your brothers if these chewed socks are **theirs**.

12. Add speech marks.

    Who, asked Mum, is going to take him for a walk?

MY SCORE

WEEK 30

Day 2

1. Circle the command verb.

   Hang your bags on a hook.

2. Tick.

   statement ☐   question ☐   command ☐

   Have you followed my instruction?

3. Rearrange the letters to spell a word that means **something you might do in science to prove an idea.**

   ┌─────────────────────────┐
   │ e   │ p e m e r i x t e n
   └─────────────────────────┘

4. Add *ity* to **humid** to make a noun.

   ┌─────────────────────────────────┐
   │   │
   └─────────────────────────────────┘

5. Write the singular of **wolves** and **hooves**.

   ┌───────────────┐ ┌───────────────┐
   │   │ │   │
   └───────────────┘ └───────────────┘

6. Which word comes before *log* in a dictionary?

   lock, lone or long ┌───────────────┐
                      │   │
                      └───────────────┘

7. Tick the meaning of the word **humid**.

   • hot and sticky   ☐

   • cold and wet   ☐

8. Add **whose** or **who's**.

   Do you know ┌───────────────┐ *bag this is and*
                 └───────────────┘

   ┌───────────────┐ *left this school tie on the bus?*
   └───────────────┘

9. Circle the collective noun.

   The class of children were very irresponsible.

10. Circle the adverb.

    If you look carefully in the school's bulging lost property box, we may be able to empty it.

11. Circle the noun.

    This is the new water bottle I lost yesterday.

12. Add punctuation.

    mum had only bought me that water bottle last tuesday.

Day 3

1. Circle the command verbs.

   Take out your books and open them at page four.

2. Tick.

   statement ☐   question ☐   command ☐

   Today we are learning about volcanoes.

3. Circle the spelling error and rewrite correctly.

   Chocolate is very populer.

   ┌─────────────────────────────────────┐
   │   │
   └─────────────────────────────────────┘

4. Add *ity* to **pure** to make a noun.

   ┌─────────────────────────────────────┐
   │   │
   └─────────────────────────────────────┘

5. Circle the incorrect plurals.

   salmons   feet   trousers   father-in-laws

6. Which word comes before **marble** in a dictionary?

   march   mark   manner ┌───────────────┐
                         │   │
                         └───────────────┘

7. Tick the meaning of the word **marble**.

   • a smooth stone   ☐

   • a dark, black wood ☐

8. Add **who's** or **whose**.

   I don't know ┌───────────────┐ *bag it is, but if*

   you ask Emma, she may know ┌───────────────┐
   lost their tie.   └───────────────┘

9. Circle the collective noun.

   Emma said that it was her tie; she had left it on a stack of chairs.

10. Circle the adverb.

    She will need to act more responsibly.

11. Circle three nouns (one is an abstract noun).

    She won't have any food if her lunch doesn't have her name on it.

12. Add speech marks.

    Oh dear! she cried. I need my things.

MY SCORE ☐ | **MY SCORE** ☐

Day 4

1. Circle the command verb.

   Give me that ball.

2. Tick.

   statement ☐   question ☐   command ☐

   I will leave it under my desk until school is finished.

3. Rearrange the letters to spell a word that means **widely known.**

   [f_____]   s a m u o f

4. Add **ure** to **depart** to make a noun.

   [_____]

5. Complete the simile.

   as [_____] as nails

6. Shorten **they** and **would**. [_____]

7. Circle the correct word.

   *I waited in **vain/vein** for my train to arrive.*

8. An opposite of **accuse** is [_____].

   blame   defend   charge

9. **These** or **Those**?

   [_____] people over there are waiting for the train.

10. Add the correct forms of the adjective.

    I think some new trains are quiet, modern cars are

    [_____], but yachts are the

    [_____].

11. What does the pronoun **it** refer to? [_____]

    This track goes to York, then it continues on to London.

12. Add punctuation.

    My friends said that italian trains were often not on time, but I didn't have this problem when I was in europe.

    [MY SCORE]

Day 5

1. Circle the command verbs.

   Stop and look at me.

2. Tick.

   statement ☐   question ☐   command ☐

   Where are you going?

3. Correct the spelling error.

   The art mewseem has lots of famous paintings.

   [_____]

4. Add **ure** to **close** to make a noun.

   [_____]

5. Complete the simile.

   as [_____] as a feather

6. Shorten **it** and **will**. [_____]

7. Circle the correct word.

   *Don't **waist/waste** water, it's precious.*

8. A similar meaning to **cunning** is

   silly   sneaky   stupid   [_____].

9. **These** or **those**?

   [_____] taps here save water, but

   [_____] over on that shelf don't.

10. Add the correct forms of the adjective.

    Not wasting any water is good, saving water is

    [_____], finding more water is

    the [_____]

11. Does the pronoun **them** refer to the **taps**?

    [_____]

    Water-saving taps are good; we need to buy more of them.

12. Add punctuation.

    Engineers from canada have helped many people in india obtain a supply of clean water.

    [MY SCORE]

WEEK 31

Who are the Owners?

The builders' tools   The children's toys   The cyclists' helmets

Do these things belong to one or more people?

Remember: The 'tail' of the apostrophe points to the owners.

The words used for the owner are plural nouns. This means:

- the tools belong to more than one builder.
- the toys belong to more than one child.
- the helmets belong to more than one cyclist.

When we want to show that something belongs to more than one person or thing, and the word already ends in 's', then we only add an apostrophe (not another 's').

If the plural noun ends in a letter other than s (like children), we add an apostrophe then s.

An apostrophe is never used to show a plural noun.

✔ the builders' tools   ✗ the builders tool's

Practice Questions

1. Is there one or more bird? [ ]

   The birds' nests were filled with tiny eggs.

2. Circle the correct sentence.

   The birds' eggs.   The birds eggs'.

1. Is there one or more main character/s? [ ]

   The main characters' performances were excellent.

2. Circle the correct sentence.

   The characters' costumes.

   The characters costumes'.

3. Correct the spelling error.

   How much firther is it to the zoo?

   [ ]

4. Add **anti** to **social** and **climax**.

   [ ]   [ ]

5. Which word has the same singular and plural?

   mouse   salmon   hammer   [ ]

6. Write the word which is spelt correctly.

   skillful   skilful   [ ]

7. Circle the correct word.

   Let me finish my work in **piece/peace.**

8. Circle the correct word.

   The farmer works (**busy, busily**) from morning to evening.

9. Write the question word.

   [ ] is his farm located?

10. Circle three pronouns.

    The farm was his for many years before he sold it.

11. Which verb group is in the past tense? Circle it.

    The old farmer will be sad because he has sold the farm.

12. Add speech marks.

    Maybe one day, he said sadly, I can return to the farm again.

MY SCORE

Day 2

1. Does the apostrophe tell you that there is one or more than one pet? ☐

   Owners need to think about their pets' safety and to make sure they don't run onto roads.

2. Circle the correct sentence.

   The children's pets.

   The childrens pets'.

3. Rearrange the letters to spell a word meaning *a trip*.

   ☐ j _____ j r o u e n y

4. What is the root word of this family?

   various   variable   varied   varying

   _____

5. Complete the simile.

   as _____ as grass

6. *Didn't* is shortened from

   _____ and _____ .

7. Circle the most suitable verb.

   *I watch in horror as the vase (**fall/falls**) from the table.*

8. *was* or *were*?

   I know it _____ *you because I saw you drop it.*

9. Add the missing word. ***who/that/whose.***

   Is that the man _____ *fixed the broken vase?*

10. Add the words needed to complete the sentence: ***to, on, at*** or ***in***.

    Mum had taken the vase _____ *the shop to be repaired.*

11. Write the feminine noun. _____

    My grandmother had offered to help, but she couldn't work out the pieces.

12. Add a comma.

    When we got home Mum was very angry with me.

    MY SCORE ☐

Day 3

1. Is there one or more friends? ☐

   All my friends' houses have gas or electric fires.

2. Circle the correct sentence.

   The children's homes.

   The childrens homes'.

3. Circle the spelling error and rewrite it correctly.

   I believe I need the exersice.

   _____

4. Add *dys* meaning bad or abnormal to *functional*.

   _____

5. Circle the incorrect plural.

   brushes   splashes   flashes   crashs

6. Write the word that is spelt correctly.

   willful   wilful   _____

7. Circle the correct word.

   *They will **except/accept** the talented new athlete.*

8. Circle the correct word.

   *The athlete fell (**heavy, heavily**) on his back.*

9. Write the question word.

   _____ *happened to him?*

10. Circle three pronouns.

    The record was his until they tripped him.

11. Which verb group is in the present tense? Circle it.

    The spectators are calling for a foul, but the umpire will make the decision.

12. Add speech marks.

    You, said the umpire firmly, will sit on the bench for the rest of the match.

    MY SCORE ☐

Day 4

1. Does the apostrophe tell you that there is one or more than one book?

   The books' titles are printed in large letters on the covers.

2. Circle the correct sentence.

   The libraries' books.

   The libraries books'.

3. Rearrange the letters to spell a word meaning **something with dates.**

   c   clanedra

4. What is the root word of this family?

   completion   incomplete   completely

5. Which word completes the simile? **shine** or **sing**

   like a diamond

6. **Don't** is shortened from

   and   .

7. Circle the correct verb.

   *They (**think, thinks**) that their team is the best.*

8. **was** or **were**?

   One team much better *than the other.*

9. Add the missing word. **who/that/whose.**

   I play for the team jersey is red.

10. Add the words needed to complete the sentence: **to, for, on** or **in.**

    Both teams are the field waiting to *start the match.*

11. Write the masculine noun.

    My father was watching from the sideline.

12. Add a comma.

    Before the match the team captains shook hands.

    MY SCORE

Day 5

1. Is there more than one coach?

   The coaches' training sessions were very tough.

2. Circle the correct sentence.

   The teams' jerseys.

   The teams jersey's.

3. Circle the spelling error and rewrite it correctly.

   That's strange and perculiar.

4. Does the **dis** in **disallow** mean bad or not?

5. Which word has the same singular and plural?

   computer   person   trousers

6. Write the word that is spelt correctly.

   stressful   stressfull

7. Circle the correct word.

   *The hungry mouse spied the **piece/peace** of cheese.*

8. Circle the correct word.

   *The mouse ran (**quick, quickly**) towards the tasty treat.*

9. Write the question word.

   was this cheese left on the table?

10. Circle three pronouns.

    The mistake was mine, I forgot to put it away.

11. Which verb group is in the past tense? Circle it.

    Dad will buy a mouse trap when he has finished work.

12. Add speech marks.

    Please, I begged, please don't hurt the mouse!

    MY SCORE

Day 1

1. Correct the spelling error.

   I need to reach the summit of the montan.

2. Add *ing* to *explode*.

3. What is the root word of this family?

   useable   useless   misuse

4. What is the plural of *snowman*?

5. Which word comes before *boost* in a dictionary?

   book   boot   bought

6. Circle the correct word.

   The plants had grown/groan wild at the abandoned house.

7. Write the question word.

   used to live in that house?

8. Circle the command verbs.

   Please go and cut those hedges.

9. Write the verb and the adverb that describes *how*.

   The gardeners skilfully cut the hedges into shape.

10. Circle the conjunction.

    Although there was still a lot of work to do, the gardeners took a rest.

11. Does the apostrophe tell you that there is one or more than one gardener?

    The gardeners' tools were left on the grass.

12. Add commas.

    By the end of the day, the gardeners cut the hedges mowed the lawn cleared the gutters and planted flowers.

MY SCORE

Day 2

1. Rearrange the letters to spell a word that means to *live in an area.*

   i   *h i n t a b i*

2. Add *er* to *happy*.

3. Add *dis* to *allow* and *continue*.

4. What is the plural of *great-grandmother*?

5. Shorten *will not.*

6. Circle the correct word.

   We bought/brought the ingredients from the shop.

7. *am* or *are*?

   I   learning how to cook.

8. Circle the correct one.

   My mum is the best/most best cook.

9. Add the words needed to complete the sentence: *to, for, on* or *in*.

   We cook dinner   our new oven.

10. Circle the conjunction.

    Mum and I wash the dishes while we wait for dinner to be ready.

11. Add a comma.

    While Mum washed I dried.

12. Add speech marks.

    Thanks Mum, I said, for teaching me how to make this tasty dinner.

MY SCORE

Day 3

1. Correct the spelling error.

   We have a long jurney to complete.

2. Add *ly* to *natural*.

3. What is the root word of this family?

   taken   overtake   taking

4. What is the plural of *football*?

5. Which word comes after *trousers* in a dictionary?

   trust   trouble   troupe

6. Circle the correct word.

   I enjoy listening to all kinds of music accept/ except heavy metal.

7. Write the question word.

   is your favourite type of music?

8. Circle the command verbs.

   Stop that loud music and come downstairs!

9. Write the verb and the adverb that describes *how*.

   I stomped down the stairs angrily.

10. Circle the conjunction.

    I wanted to listen to my music because I was having a bad day.

11. Does the apostrophe tell you that there is one or more than one parent?

    Seeing my parents' kind smiles made me feel better.

12. Add commas.

    Later, my parents and I listened to rap pop classical and techno music together.

    MY SCORE

Day 4

1. Rearrange the letters to spell a word that means *break so it can't be used again.*

   d   t e s y d o r

2. Add *ible* to *sense* and *reverse*.

3. Add *mis* to *spell* and *calculate*.

4. What is the plural of *daughter-in-law*?

5. Shorten *cannot.*

6. Circle the correct word.

   We bought/brought our pet dog on our holiday.

7. *am* or *are*?

   We   going on holiday soon.

8. Circle the correct one.

   Packing for a holiday is the worst/most worst.

9. Add the words needed to complete the sentence: *to, for, on* or *at*.

   Our flight is   six o'clock tonight.

10. Circle the conjunction.

    We will need to set an early alarm if we want to be on time.

11. Add a comma.

    Unless you want to be tired you had better go to bed now.

12. Add speech marks.

    But, Mum, the small girl complained, I'm not tired!

    MY SCORE

Day 5

1. Circle the spelling errors and rewrite them correctly.

   Nun of us got into truble.

   [   ] [   ]

2. Add *ous* to *glory* and *vary*.

   [   ] [   ]

3. What is the root word of this family?

   agreeable   disagree   agreement

   [   ]

4. What is the plural of *toothbrush*?

   [   ]

5. Which word comes before *chimney* in a dictionary?

   chimpanzee   chin   chick   [   ]

6. Circle the correct word.

   *The girl let out a loud **grown/groan** as she stood on her sore foot.*

7. Write the question word.

   [   ] *did you hurt your foot?*

8. Circle the command verbs.

   Sit down and rest.

9. Write the verb and the adverb that describes *how*.

   She carefully lifted her foot on to the cushion.

   [   ] [   ]

10. Circle the conjunction.

    She seems happy although her foot is very painful.

11. Does the apostrophe tell you that there is one or more than one girl? [   ]

    The girl's parents called a doctor.

12. Add a comma.

    The doctor told the girl that she would need to rest her foot ice it and keep it elevated.

    [MY SCORE]

Skill Focus Review

1. Rearrange the letters to spell a word that means *a long winter sleep.*

   [h   ] t i n e r b a h e

2. Add *acy* to *private* to make a noun.

   [   ]

3. Complete the simile.

   as [   ] as an ox

4. What is the plural of *runner-up*?

   [   ]

5. Circle the correct word.

   *Did you **hear/here** the singer's beautiful voice?*

6. Circle the correct word.

   *The word aunt is a **feminine/masculine** noun.*

7. Change these adjectives to the correct form used to compare things.

   good [   ] [   ]

   bad [   ] [   ]

8. Circle the noun.

   She is a great singer.

9. Write the command verbs.

   Go and sit in your seat, the show is about to start.

   [   ] [   ]

10. Add the missing pronoun.

    The musical ran for 50 minutes before [   ] *finally ended.*

11. Does the apostrophe tell you that there is one or more than one singer? [   ]

    The singers' performance.

12. Add speech marks.

    That, I remarked, was the most beautiful voice I have ever heard.

    [MY SCORE]

NOTES